Teaching Reading in Science

A Supplement to *Teaching Reading in the Content Areas Teacher's Manual (2nd Edition)*

Mary Lee Barton
Deborah L. Jordan

Mid-continent Research for Education and Learning
2550 S. Parker Road, Suite 500 Aurora, CO 80014-1678
303.337.0990 • 303.337.3005

Teaching Reading in Science
A Supplement to *Teaching Reading in the Content Areas: If Not Me, Then Who?*
2nd Edition
MARY LEE BARTON
DEBORAH L. JORDAN

This publication is based on work sponsored wholly, or in part, by the U.S. Department of Education National Eisenhower Mathematics and Science Programs, Office of Educational Research and Improvement (OERI), under Grant Number R319A000004B. The content of this publication does not necessarily reflect the views of OERI or the Department of Education or any other agency of the U.S. Government.

To purchase additional copies of this book, contact

Association for Supervision and Curriculum Development
1703 N. Beauregard St. • Alexandria, VA. 22311-1714 USA
Telephone: 800-933-2723 or 703-578-9600 • Fax: 703-575-5400
Web site: http://www.ascd.org • E-mail: member@ascd.org

Discounts for bulk purchases are available.

ASCD Stock number #302269
ISBN-10: 1-893476-03-0
ISBN-13: 978-1-893476-03-5

Prices: ASCD member, $20.95; nonmember, $22.95

Table of Contents

Acknowledgments

A number of people contributed to the production of this document. In particular, the authors would like to acknowledge Mid-continent Research for Education and Learning staff, specifically Alice Krueger, who constructed the secondary level examples in Section 5; Linda Brannan and Terry Young, who helped with the literature search; Norma Brown, who oversaw copyright permissions; quality assurance reviewers John Sutton, Clare Heidema, Elaine DeBassige D'Amato, Barb Gaddy, Vicki LaRock, Jane Doty, and Dan Seger; editor Vicki Urquhart; and Leah Dixon and Molly Drew, who performed the desktop publishing portion of this project. The authors would also like to acknowledge outside reviewers Marcia Daab, Nancy Kellogg, and Emily CoBabe.

Rationale

Ask students to take out their science textbooks, and what response do you typically get? Groans? Sighs? Comments that are less than enthusiastic?

This reaction is understandable. For many students, reading science is like reading a foreign language. A high school chemistry text can contain some 3,000 new vocabulary terms — far more than are taught in most foreign language classes (Holliday, 1991). In addition, it's not unusual for science textbooks to have a readability level one or two years above the grade level in which they are used. Finally, many textbooks aren't particularly user friendly. This is often the case when they are written by content-area experts without the assistance of professional writers or experienced practitioners who could help ensure that ideas were communicated clearly.

Science teachers, themselves, appear to feel somewhat ambivalent about textbook usage. Although teachers agree that students need to be able to read science, 28 percent of elementary teachers surveyed nationwide in 1998 reported using textbooks only as a reference source; 33 percent reported rarely or never using textbooks (Tolman, Hardy, & Sudweeks, 1998).

Why do teachers feel so ambivalent about textbooks? One possible reason is students' inability to read these texts. Another is that the content of science textbooks can become outdated more quickly than, say, an American literature textbook, rendering these books less useful as the years go by. A third reason cited by critics of science textbooks is that textbooks emphasize product rather than process (Donahue, 2000). In an inquiry-based approach to learning that accompanied the post-Sputnik era of the 1960s, science education has focused largely on *doing* science rather than reading science.

Many educators contend that when students *do* science, they are more engaged in learning than when they read science text. When students actively participate in science, they are involved in collaboration, exploration, and problem solving. Hands-on science activities give students opportunities to

- wrestle with science problems;
- work together to generate and test hypotheses; and
- analyze data, draw conclusions, and write about their findings.

In fact, reading science text and textbooks requires the same critical thinking, analysis, and active engagement as performing hands-on science activities. Science and reading have many process skills in common. As Armbruster (1993) contends, "The same skills that make good scientists also make good readers: engaging prior knowledge, forming hypotheses, establishing plans, evaluating understanding, determining the relative importance of information, describing patterns, comparing and contrasting, making inferences, drawing conclusions, generalizing, evaluating sources, and so on" (p. 347).

In this supplement, as in the *Teaching Reading in the Content Areas (TRCA) Teacher's Manual*, we present the latest research on reading and learning in science. We also include suggestions on how to help students confront the unique challenges of constructing meaning from science textbooks and on how to embed explicit science reading instruction within the natural context of science instruction in the classroom. Throughout this supplement, you will find references to sections or pages of the *TRCA Teacher's Manual* that provide a more thorough discussion of a topic or another example of a reading strategy.

In Section 5 of this supplement, you will find references to the five phases of learning — *engage*, *explore*, *explain*, *elaborate*, and *evaluate* — which are common components of science instructional models. Science teachers are encouraged to use the "5E" approach or instructional models that share these components to build students' in-depth understanding of science concepts and strengthen their thinking skills (see Section 3, pp. 39–44 for more about the five phases of learning). Reading science texts and other materials is an important part of this process. For students to gain understanding, teachers need to use a variety of strategies, including those that involve manipulative, interactive, and physical materials, to address science content in depth and avoid focusing on isolated or disconnected facts.

Section 1

Three Interactive Elements of Reading

Three Interactive Elements of Reading

Reader

Climate

Text Features

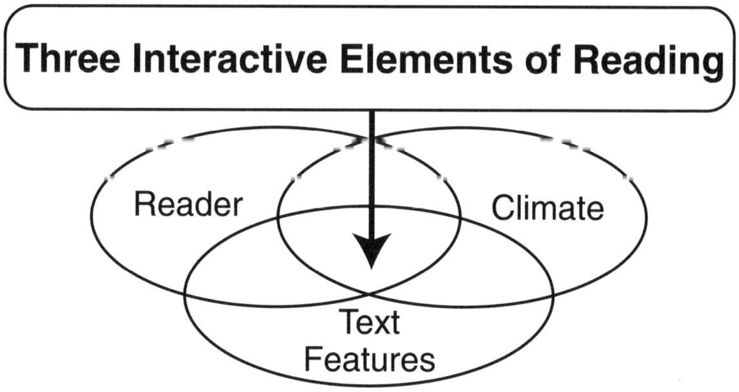

Introduction

Writers Santa, Havens, and Harrison (1996) state it well: "Most students arrive at the science teacher's classroom knowing how to read, but few understand how to use reading for learning science content" (p. 166). One explanation for this disparity is that students most often learn the reading process using narrative text. They haven't been taught that reading science requires different reading and thinking skills than reading fiction. Certainly, informational text — and science text, in particular — presents unique challenges to novice readers. Thus, one of the first steps for teachers is to help students understand that reading science text requires them to use different skills than they may have used in the past.

In addition to the general reading skills needed to comprehend narrative text, readers of science text also must be able to apply the following knowledge and skills:

- Understand specialized vocabulary terms and phrases that are unique to science.
- Understand vocabulary terms and phrases that have different meanings when used in science.
- Interpret scientific symbols and diagrams.

Notes

Notes

- Recognize and understand organizational patterns common to science texts.
- Make sense of text using text structure and page layout that may not be user friendly.
- Infer implied sequences and recognize cause-and-effect relationships.
- Infer main ideas and draw conclusions that may not be explicitly stated.
- Use inductive and deductive reasoning skills.

These skills are discussed in more detail in the sections that follow, which also include suggestions for planning instruction that will help students become more effective consumers of science reading material. As in the *TRCA Teacher's Manual*, this supplement discusses teaching reading in science in terms of three interactive elements that affect comprehension: the reader, the climate, and text features.

The Role of the Reader

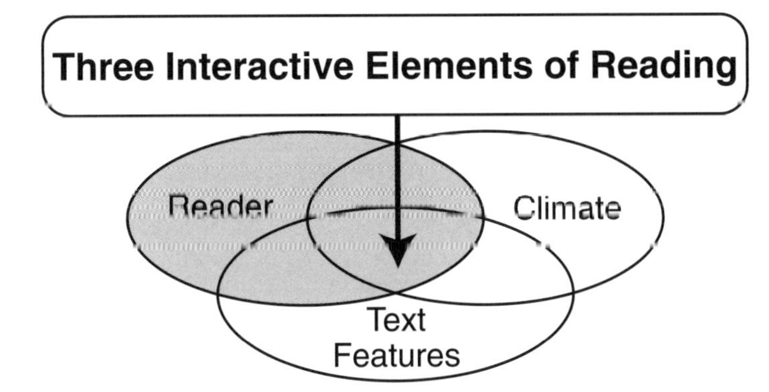

Things to Think About

1. How do students' experiences and prior knowledge of science affect their learning?
2. How can teachers help students recognize and change any misconceptions they have about science?
3. How can teachers motivate students to learn and practice reading strategies?

Prior Knowledge

For students to make sense of what they read, they need to be able to grasp and make sense of new information in light of what they already know. When readers activate and use their prior knowledge, they make the necessary connections between what they know and new information. Teachers should help students recognize the important role that prior knowledge plays and teach them to use that knowledge when learning science through reading.

Teachers can show students how to activate prior knowledge by demonstrating basic pre-reading techniques such as

- brainstorming ideas that a topic brings to mind;
- previewing a passage, noting headings and bold print; and
- constructing a graphic organizer, web, or outline from passage headings for use in note taking.

Notes

Teachers also need to ensure that their students have the prior knowledge and experience they need to make these connections. Discovering what students already know about a topic helps teachers design instruction around the missing knowledge. A number of strategies can help teachers determine what students know before they begin studying a new topic:

- Semantic Mapping (p. 61)
- Word Sort (p. 69)
- Anticipation Guide (p. 72)
- Directed Reading/Thinking Activity (p. 76)
- K-W-L (p. 91)
- Problematic Situation (p. 99)
- Learning Log (p. 114)

Prior knowledge must not only be adequate for learning to occur, it also must be accurate. Unfortunately, sometimes students come to their science classes with a number of misconceptions about topics they will be studying. Helping students confront and resolve their misconceptions requires concentrated effort on the part of teachers and students. The strategies listed above can help teachers identify students' misconceptions.

Another strategy that addresses students' misconceptions is the extended anticipation guide (Duffelmeyer & Baum, 1992). This strategy requires learners to identify their beliefs prior to reading and to justify these ideas — or revise them — when they read information in the text that supports or contradicts their understanding. (See pp. 72–75 in this supplement for instructions on using this strategy in the classroom.) Because letting go of misconceptions is so difficult, this issue is extensively addressed in Section 3, "Strategic Teaching."

Mental Disposition

Exemplary science educators know that students' attitudes about reading and learning science affect their achievement. Of particular concern, then, are reports that students' motivation to learn wanes over time. For example, Holloway (1999) notes that "intrinsic motivation for literacy and other academic subjects declines in middle school" (p. 80). What can teachers do to increase students' motivation to learn from reading science text?

In addition to connecting reading assignments to students' real-world experiences, teachers need to show students that becoming effective consumers of science text has value. Students need to see firsthand that practicing the right reading strategies will improve their achievement.

This is especially true of struggling readers. Some of these students also have a poor attitude toward reading and often don't see the connection between the effort they put forth to read and complete their assignments and the grades they earn in class. Marzano, Pickering, and Pollock (2001) cite a set of studies demonstrating that simply showing students that added effort improves their achievement actually increases students' achievement. The authors note that since "students might not be aware of the importance of believing in effort," teachers should "explicitly teach and exemplify the connection between effort and achievement" (p. 51).

Instructional Implications

To demonstrate to students how their effort affects their achievement, Marzano et al. (2001) suggest that students periodically assess their level of effort on assignments and track the impact of their effort on the grades they earn. Teachers can give students a set of effort and achievement rubrics (see Exhibit 1 on p. 6), which students can use to assess their effort and achievement. In addition, a chart (see Exhibit 2 on p. 7) can be provided so students can record and track their progress.

Notes

When students observe the impact that their effort and attitude have on their progress, they begin to see the value of applying reading strategies to improve their comprehension and learning. They also gain a sense of control over their learning — a crucial step in assuming more responsibility for their own learning.

Exhibit 1. Effort and Achievement Rubrics

Effort and Achievement Rubrics for Science

Scale: 4 = excellent; 3 = good;
2 = needs improvement; 1 = unacceptable

Effort Rubric

4 I worked on my science assignment until it was completed. I pushed myself to continue working on the task even when difficulties arose, when a solution was not immediately evident, or when I had trouble understanding what an author was saying. I used obstacles that arose as opportunities to strengthen my understanding and skills beyond the minimum required to complete the assignment.

3 I worked on my science assignment until it was completed. I pushed myself to continue working on the task even when difficulties arose, when a solution was not immediately apparent, or when I had trouble understanding what an author was saying.

2 I put some effort into my science assignment, but I stopped working when difficulties arose, when a solution was not immediately evident, or when I had trouble understanding what an author was saying.

1 I put very little effort into my science assignment.

Achievement Rubric

4 I exceeded the objectives of the assignment.

3 I met the objectives of the assignment.

2 I met a few of the objectives of the assignment, but didn't meet others.

1 I did not meet the objectives of the assignment.

Exhibit 2. Effort and Achievement Chart

Notes

Student Jon Starek	Assignment	Effort Rubric	Achievement Rubric
Monday, Sept. 21	Study and describe parts of three different flowering plants. Read text about plant parts and find parts on actual plants to complete worksheet.	4	4
Wed., Sept. 23	Homework: Read the article "How Plants Grow."	3	3
Thurs, Sept. 24	Write a two-page narrative on key points made in the article and how these reinforce or conflict with what I thought I knew about how plants grow.	3	3
Fri., Sept. 25	Read text pages on experimental design and design experiment on germination rate of plants.	3	3

Notes

The Role of Climate

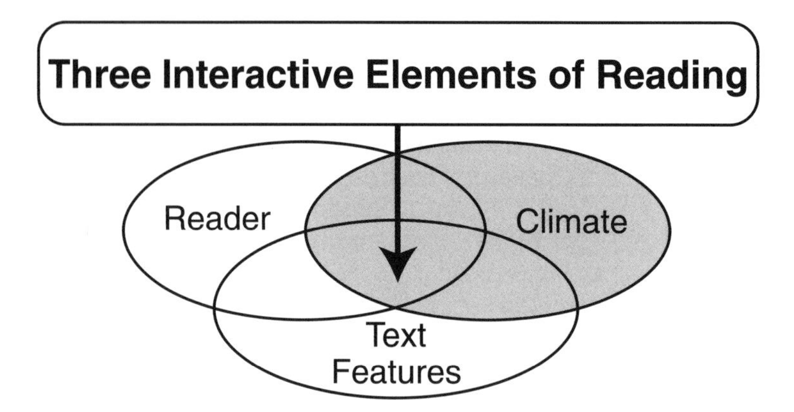

Things to Think About

1. How does climate affect students' attitude toward learning science?
2. What do effective science teachers do to create a classroom climate that is conducive to learning?

A fifth grade teacher always begins the year by asking her class this simple question: "What is science?" The varied responses students give usually cover three basic themes:

> *"Science is fun. It's doing experiments and watching butterflies emerge from their chrysalises."*
>
> *"Science is reading boring textbooks. I hate it."*
>
> *"Science is watching movies or videos."*

What shapes students' attitudes about science? Certainly, students' attitudes are deeply affected by the climate in which they learn. Teachers' beliefs, attitudes, and values help to create the climate in which children develop their own feelings about subject matter. In fact, as early as the fifth grade, students have developed definite attitudes about science. Sadly, many students graduate from high school despising science, considering it boring and too difficult. As the authors of *Science for All Americans* (Rutherford & Ahlgren, 1990) note, "They see science only as an academic activity, not as a way of understanding the world in which they live" (p. 186).

Given the effect that attitude has on learning, it's essential that science teachers create a positive classroom climate. The term *climate*

refers not only to the affective dimensions discussed in the *TRCA Teacher's Manual,* but also to physical dimensions. As Program Standard D of the *National Science Education Standards* (National Research Council [NRC], 1996) asserts, "The K–12 science program must give students access to appropriate and sufficient resources, including quality teachers, time, materials, and equipment, adequate and safe space, and the community" (p. 218).

The climate in today's exemplary science classrooms is grounded in the high standards and vision described in the *National Science Education Standards* (NRC, 1996): "All students, regardless of age, sex, cultural or ethnic background, disabilities, aspirations, or interest and motivation in science, should have the opportunity to attain high levels of scientific literacy" (p. 20). Science instruction is no longer viewed solely as preparation for college-bound students. Today's science students come from all walks of life and have a wide range of backgrounds and experiences.

What constitutes an effective learning environment? According to the NRC (2000), an effective learning environment is characterized by four dimensions:

- **Learner centered:** Respecting and understanding students' prior experiences and understandings and using them to build new understandings.
- **Knowledge centered:** Helping students focus on the "big" ideas and "develop well-organized bodies of knowledge and organize that knowledge so that it supports planning and strategic thinking" (p. 122).
- **Assessment centered:** Helping students learn to monitor and regulate their own learning, to think critically, and to receive instruction that is informed and supported.
- **Community centered:** Requiring students to "articulate their ideas, challenge the ideas of others, and negotiate deeper meaning along with other learners" (p. 122).

Notes

Notes

Instructional Implications

What can teachers do to ensure that their classrooms incorporate these elements?

Learner centered

To ensure that the classroom environment is learner-centered, teachers should consider the individual needs of their students. As each lesson is planned, it's important to consider the extent to which each student has the background knowledge needed to understand the concepts that will be taught. This step may point to the need to create learning experiences that provide students with additional information about particular concepts prior to giving them reading assignments.

Engaging students in concrete learning activities can help prepare them to learn more abstract ideas. These activities can introduce students to concepts, which will then be reinforced, confirmed, or enriched through reading. Consider using an anticipation guide, DR/TA, K-W-L, problematic situation, graphic organizer, PLAN, or other pre-reading activities to activate, build, and reinforce background knowledge students need in order to make connections while reading. (See Section 5, pp. 49–125 of this supplement for these pre-reading strategies.)

Knowledge centered

In a knowledge-centered learning environment, students are offered a variety of opportunities to learn about the discipline of science. Teachers help students recognize the "big ideas" in science and differentiate between main ideas and supporting material in their science textbooks. They also ask students to use this knowledge to make connections among these ideas and apply them in new situations. As discussed in the next section, "The Role of Text Features," science text can be difficult for even experienced readers. Teachers should reread text material that they plan to assign to see if

main ideas are expressed clearly and if the relationships among ideas are evident.

To get the most out of their science textbooks, students must understand how the information is organized and how the concepts presented relate to one another (Misulis, 1997). Teachers can provide students with graphic organizers that will help them recognize and understand relationships among the ideas they read in their texts. In addition, teachers should incorporate questioning and reflection strategies that focus students' attention on understanding knowledge derived from the text and on making connections between what they have observed and what they have read. A number of strategies, including reciprocal teaching, learning logs, and question-answer relationships, are designed to clarify students' understanding of what is presented in class and in their textbooks. (See Section 5 of this supplement for these strategies.)

Assessment centered

Assessment-centered classrooms encourage students to monitor and regulate their learning in response to feedback from self-assessment and teachers' assessments. Learning to monitor and regulate their own learning is a skill that can benefit students throughout their education — indeed, throughout their lives.

There are many ways to teach and reinforce students' self-assessment skills. For example, teachers can encourage students to assess their own learning by collecting data, comparing results with others, and applying what they have learned. As students become adept at monitoring their learning, they will be better equipped to assess their understanding of text and to monitor and regulate their understanding as they read.

Teachers can encourage the art of self-evaluation in a number of ways. First, they can model for students how they monitor their understanding when reading and learning new information. In addition, teachers can ask students to reflect on their learning using

Notes

Notes

writing-to-learn activities or leading discussions about what learning strategies are most effective when comprehension problems arise.

Finally, teachers should explain — and model — that assessment activities offer learners and their teachers valuable feedback. For example, instead of simply grading and returning students' lab reports, teachers might note areas that need further work and require students to use these comments to make any needed revisions. Thoughtful educators also use assessment results to revise their instructional approaches. In this way, they treat assessment not as a product, but rather as part of an ongoing process that supports learning and informs instruction.

Community centered

A community-centered classroom offers students a safe environment in which they can learn from their mistakes and from one another. One way to begin to create this kind of environment is to give students extra credit for sharing their confusion and questions about what they have read, a strategy suggested by Schoenbach, Greenleaf, Cziko, and Hurwitz (1999). The authors also suggest telling students that the more explicit they are about where in a text they got lost or why they think something is difficult for them to understand, the more credit they will receive. The benefits of this strategy are many. For one, talking with others can help students more specifically identify the questions they have or the topics they find confusing. Second, classroom dialogue and conversation help develop a sense of community among students and between students and the teacher. Another strategy suggested by Schoenbach et al. (1999) is to invite students to bring in reading materials that will "stump" the teacher so the teacher can model "think-alouds," which lets students know that teachers, too, often have to use strategies to understand what they are reading.

In summary, the characteristics of science learning present a unique challenge — and opportunity — for science teachers as they design

the classroom learning environment. By identifying individual students' needs, helping students to focus on "big ideas," using assessment as a springboard for learning, and creating a community in which students learn and deepen their understanding together, teachers can help ensure that students leave their classes with a positive view of the benefits of learning science.

Notes

Notes

The Role of Text Features

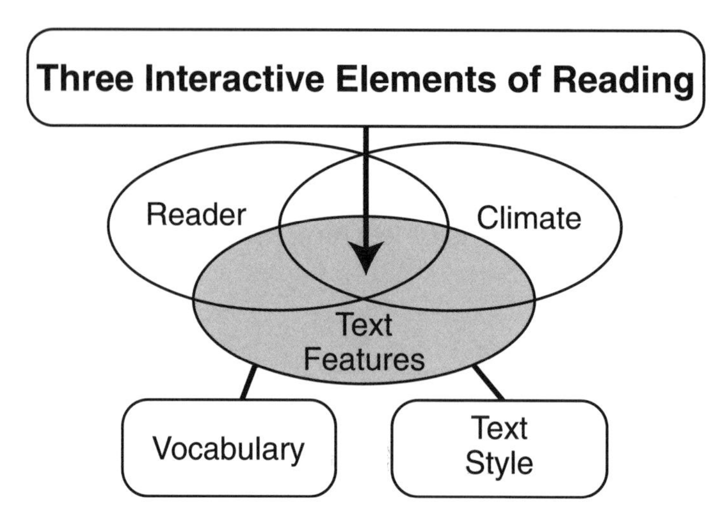

Text features are those aspects of text content and presentation that influence comprehension. In this section, we focus first on vocabulary and then on text style.

Text Features: Vocabulary

Things to Think About

1. How important is vocabulary instruction in science classes?
2. How should teachers determine which science terms students really need to know?
3. What are the best ways to develop students' understanding of science terminology?

Vocabulary development is crucial for students in all subject areas, but it is especially important for science students. As noted earlier, science textbook authors pack their writing with concepts that are unfamiliar to many students. For example, high school chemistry texts can contain some 3,000 new terms. The challenge of learning so many new words is compounded by the fact that learners have no existing schema, or mental framework, to help them grasp the meaning of these new terms and phrases.

Although science teachers may be aware of the need for students to learn science terms and phrases, they may not know the most effective ways to help students learn these words. Consequently, many teachers

resort to teaching vocabulary the way they were taught: looking words up in a dictionary and memorizing their definitions.

We know now that this method doesn't provide learners with an adequate understanding of science terminology. Moreover, it reduces vocabulary instruction to an activity that is seemingly unrelated to the rest of instruction. Students need to be able to construct meaning — to wrestle with their understanding of a word's meaning in terms of their prior knowledge and in terms of how the word "fits" into, or relates to, other academic content they are learning. As Vacca and Vacca (1999) write, "Teaching words well means giving students multiple opportunities to learn how words are conceptually related to one another in the material they are studying" (p. 315).

One goal of vocabulary instruction is to prepare students to read and understand science text materials. Another goal is to develop students' understanding of science concepts so they are able to communicate about these ideas. Given the great number of new terms and students' insufficient prior knowledge, a challenge for teachers is determining the best way to approach vocabulary instruction in the science classroom. There are four steps that science teachers can follow to plan such instruction:

1. Identify specific learning goals for the unit.
2. Develop each unit's vocabulary list based on these goals.
3. Determine the level of understanding students need for the listed terms.
4. Select appropriate vocabulary development strategies.

1. Identify Learning Goals for the Unit

The first step in planning a unit of instruction is to identify specific learning goals and objectives. This may include identifying particular standards and benchmarks that students should meet by the end of the unit. Specifying the knowledge and skills that students will learn

Notes

during the unit helps guide the process of pulling together the list of vocabulary terms and phrases to focus on during the unit.

2. Develop the Vocabulary List

The next step is to develop a list of the vocabulary terms and phrases that students need to learn in order to understand their textbooks and to communicate effectively about what they are learning. Most textbooks include lists of vocabulary terms associated with specific topics. One place to begin is to review and refine these lists in light of the specific standards and benchmarks associated with the unit.

Because science texts are packed with concepts, we recommend that teachers select vocabulary terms based on how critical they are to students understanding and communicating about the unit's main ideas. Holliday (1991) offers additional guidance about vocabulary selection:

> Eliminate jargon from [the] curriculum or at least reduce its importance by focusing student attention on necessary scientific language. The purpose here is not to malign any particular scientific terms but to stimulate debate among science teachers about the appropriateness of the vocabulary in science texts. … Scientific vocabulary can be jargon to students when such words are (1) used only by experts, (2) difficult to learn (even for high ability students), (3) used only for academic testing purposes, or (4) introduced too early in students' schooling. (p. 46)

3. Determine the Level of Understanding Students Need

After a vocabulary list has been developed, decide which terms students need to learn well enough to comprehend them in text, versus those that require more in-depth understanding. Depending on the learning goals identified for a unit, there may be terms that students will only encounter a few times and, thus, only need to understand at a basic level. However, there typically are key terms that students need to understand that are critical to identified standards and benchmarks.

4. Select Appropriate Vocabulary Development Strategies

Defining the degree of understanding students need to develop for various vocabulary terms and phrases helps teachers select the most appropriate instructional strategies. Certain vocabulary strategies

help learners understand the meaning of a term enough to make sense of it when they come across it while reading science text. For those terms that don't demand such in-depth understanding, teachers might use the student VOC strategy, reviewed in Section 5. This strategy provides learners with a more simplistic understanding of a concept's meaning because it doesn't require them to consider a term in relationship to other terms.

Other strategies challenge learners to explore the meaning of a term or phrase in relationship to similar concepts, giving learners a deeper, richer appreciation of its meaning. For example, concept definition mapping, the Frayer model, and semantic feature analysis (see Section 5) require that learners demonstrate their understanding of a term's meaning in relation to other similar terms. These strategies are effective tools to use throughout a unit. For example, asking students to complete concept definition maps for particular concepts at the beginning of a unit will activate their prior knowledge. As students learn more about these concepts during the unit and develop a deeper understanding of what they mean, they can revisit their initial concept definition maps and add to them. In this way, the strategy becomes a work-in-progress — a living vocabulary document — that evolves as each learner's understanding deepens.

Teachers should base their instructional decisions on the goals they set for student learning. On pages 49–71 of this supplement are science-specific examples of strategies from the *TRCA Teacher's Manual* that are best suited to teaching science vocabulary. Regardless of which strategies teachers incorporate into their lessons, there are certain generalizations that should guide the process of teaching vocabulary. The following guidelines and research are reported in *Classroom Instruction that Works* (Marzano, et al., 2001):

- ***Offer students several opportunities to encounter selected terms in context.*** Research (e.g., Jenkins, Stein, & Wysocki, 1984) on learning new words in context, without direct instruction,

Notes

demonstrates that students need to be exposed to a word at least six times before they have enough experience with the word to determine and recall its meaning.

- ***Provide instruction about key concepts prior to reading.*** Even superficial instruction increases the likelihood that students will comprehend new words when they encounter them while reading. In fact, research (e.g., Jenkins, Stein, & Wysocki, 1984) indicates that when students are given at least superficial vocabulary instruction, their ability to understand new words increases significantly.
- ***Show students how to connect an image with the new term.*** A 1980 study by Powell found that instructional techniques incorporating the use of imagery resulted in achievement gains in word knowledge that were 34 percentile points higher than techniques that did not. A sketch or symbolic representation does not have to be artistic; it only needs to mean something to the student so that he or she can connect this image with the meaning of the concept and more easily recall that meaning when needed. After students create visual images of new concepts, ask them to write definitions for these new ideas in their own words.
- ***Focus vocabulary instruction on words that are critical to new content.*** Research by Stahl and Fairbanks (1986) indicates that students' achievement may increase as much as 33 percentile points when vocabulary instruction focuses on specific words that are important to what students are learning.

Text Features: Text Style

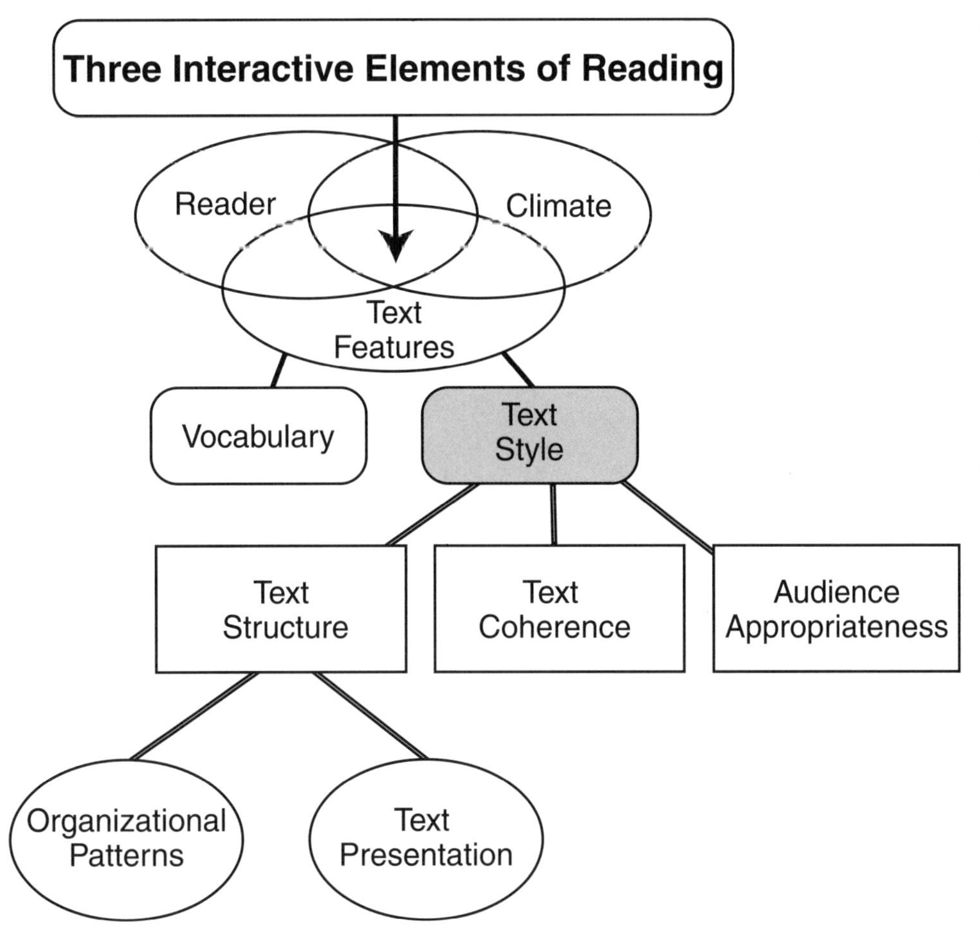

As discussed, comprehending science text depends on the interaction among three key elements: the reader, the climate, and text features. Text features that affect students' comprehension of science text — both positively and negatively — are numerous. The previous section examined one feature of science text, vocabulary, and explained how teachers can plan for and incorporate vocabulary development activities into content instruction.

This section explores text style, specifically, *text structure, text coherence*, and *audience appropriateness*. The first edition of the *TRCA Teacher's Manual* included a discussion of text structure. Since the publication of that manual, however, research and experience have shown that additional characteristics of text style have a significant impact on students' comprehension of textbooks and on teachers' selection of texts. Thus, we have expanded our vision of content-area reading instruction to include these additional components.

Notes

Notes

> ### Things to Think About
> 1. What features of science text make reading this text difficult for students?
> 2. What responsibility do science teachers have to teach students how to contend with text features such as organization and presentation?
> 3. What do science teachers need to know about text coherence and audience appropriateness so that they can select reading material that students can understand?

Text Structure

Two aspects of text structure — organization and presentation — have a direct impact on reading comprehension. Therefore, teaching students how to recognize and represent the organizational patterns commonly used by authors of science text can significantly influence students' learning. According to Jones, Palincsar, Ogle, and Carr (1987), students who understand specific organizational patterns are able to use this knowledge to

- locate key information,
- identify what is important and unimportant,
- impose some organization on text in which the organization is only implied,
- synthesize information that appears in different locations within a text or from a number of texts,
- connect new information with what is known,
- restructure schema to account for new learning, and
- organize their recall of information they read.

Similarly, acquainting students with text presentation — how textbook publishers lay out content — can enhance their comprehension. In their synthesis of research on text organization and presentation and the relationship of these text features to

students' reading comprehension, Dickson, Simmons, and Kameenui (1995) found the following:

- Well-presented physical text (i.e., text that is visually laid out in a way that makes the organization of the content evident) assists in reading comprehension.
- Text structure and students' awareness of text structure are highly related to reading comprehension.
- Explicit instruction in the physical presentation of text and/or text structure aids in reading comprehension.

Organizational Patterns

An organizational pattern is the way ideas and information are arranged in text. Of the seven organizational patterns discussed in the *TRCA Teacher's Manual*, five are often used by authors of science text:

- **Comparison/contrast:** Reporting similarities and differences between or among two or more things, such as plant and animal respiration.
- **Concept definition:** Reporting characteristics common to a concept, such as *magma*.
- **Description:** Reporting on data collection, such as observations and measurements for a specific object or experiment.
- **Generalization/principle:** Writing about a hypothesis and the support for or against it, for example, "Playing classical music near plants enhances their growth."
- **Process/cause-effect:** Reporting the characteristic steps of a process such as the life cycle, or reporting causes and effects of certain phenomena, such as global warming.

We recommend that science teachers scaffold students' learning of each pattern — that is, provide more support at the beginning stages of skill/concept formation and less support as students'

Notes

Notes

understanding deepens — using text passages that focus on content covered in class.

1. A good place to begin is to explain that learning and applying knowledge of organizational patterns improves comprehension and therefore may well reduce the amount of time students spend trying to learn from their textbooks. It's also helpful to use a particular passage to explain and illustrate that authors use particular patterns for specific reasons. For example, if an author wants to explain the similarities and differences between sedimentary and igneous rock, explain that the author might organize the information in a comparison-contrast pattern. Point out for students the key questions addressed by the pattern. In this case: What items are being compared? What is it about them that is being compared? What characteristics do they have in common? In what ways are the items different? List for students the signal words authors often use when writing in that pattern (e.g., *both, different from, however, on the other hand, similarly*).

2. Next, provide students with a one- or two-paragraph passage that exemplifies the organizational pattern. This example can be from the text or from trade materials. The pattern should be clearly evident even to novice readers. After students have read the passage once, use a think-aloud (see pp. 107–108) to model for students how to recognize which pattern is evident and how to use that knowledge to locate the main idea and determine which information in the passage is most important.

3. Then give students another passage that exemplifies the pattern, but ask them to explain how they can identify it as such (e.g., signal words and key questions). Continue the scaffolding process, asking students to do their own think-alouds with a partner using yet another example of the same organizational pattern.

4. As students better understand the characteristics of the organizational pattern, demonstrate how to capture this pattern visually. One long-used method is to outline the text for students. Another is to give them a completed graphic organizer (e.g., a web) for a sample paragraph that illustrates the hierarchical relationships among ideas. Then, using another paragraph, have students fill in a partially completed graphic organizer. Finally, ask students to use their own means of representing key ideas and relationships — either with a graphic organizer, a web, or another visual, all of which aid in recall and the construction of meaning. Graphic organizers and outlining can be effective tools to help learners locate, choose, make connections among, and restructure information in text (Jones et al., 1987).

5. Next, have students write a paragraph using the same organizational pattern. When it is clear that students can recognize the pattern and apply their knowledge to locate and recall important ideas, repeat this process with another pattern common in students' textbooks.

Text Presentation

Text presentation refers to (1) the way written material is physically laid out; (2) its visual textual cues, such as headings, captions, bold print, italics, and font size and color; and (3) its illustrations and graphics. These features can either help or hinder comprehension. Therefore, it is helpful to "walk students through" their textbook's layout at the beginning of the school year. Point out for students how the font color and size are used to help readers identify sections and subsections within chapters. Examine how the publisher uses white space to indicate a change of subject, and point this out to students. Explain that publishers try to incorporate visual cues to help readers locate important ideas. (The *TRCA Teacher's Manual* refers to these as "reader aids.") Model for students how to predict what a section of text will be about simply by reading the headings. Explain that

Notes

Notes

paying attention to this clue can help students identify the information and organizational patterns. For example, the heading "Measuring Moisture in the Air" signals a process pattern; the expert reader will adopt a mental framework, and perhaps construct a visual framework, to organize and store information about this process.

Text Coherence

Text coherence is closely related to organization. Coherence refers to the degree to which the text content is logically and clearly explained. Armbruster (1996) cites numerous studies about the influence that coherence has on comprehension. These studies found that comprehension is adversely affected when the main idea is not clearly stated, when the relationships among events are implied rather than explicit, and when irrelevant details are included. Armbruster (1996) explains: "In considerate texts, main ideas are explicitly stated. They appear in prominent places such as introductions and summaries, headings, and topic sentences at the beginning of sections and paragraphs. Main ideas should not be buried in the middle of paragraphs or left to be inferred by the reader" (p. 53).

Unfortunately, authors of science text may not follow this rule. In fact, it's not unusual for science writers to present their observations or data first, and then to pull together these ideas in a concluding statement. Novice readers struggle when asked to wade through seemingly unrelated bits of information that lack purpose or direction until the end of the passage.

Coherence also refers to the logical ordering of ideas and to the obvious relationships among the ideas. Skilled authors order their ideas in a logical sequence; for example, from most important to least important. These authors also are careful to explicitly state how causes are linked to effects. They select specific signal words to reinforce comparisons and contrasts, or to indicate sequential order.

Science teachers should spend time reviewing the text used in their classes to assess its coherence. If problems exist, they may need to identify the author's main ideas before assigning passages to be read. Teachers also may need to be sure that students understand how concepts, ideas, and phenomena discussed in the passage are related.

Audience Appropriateness

"Audience appropriateness refers to the extent to which the text matches the target readers' probable knowledge base" (Armbruster, 1996, p. 54). Teachers need to select text that builds on their students' background knowledge and that elaborates sufficiently on new concepts and phenomena using language, phrasing, and sentence structure that students can understand.

Unfortunately, some science textbooks are not audience appropriate. For example, despite the fact that educators want their students to be able to describe and explain natural phenomena, authors of science text don't always provide well-written descriptions or explanations (Finley, 1991). Science textbook authors are content-area experts who know their subject matter but frequently cannot translate this knowledge into text that can be grasped by science students:

> The expert has vast amounts of domain-relevant prior knowledge, images, and experience, and although all this was once declarative knowledge, it long ago became proceduralized, and so is also largely inaccessible to him or her. But it is needed, and in declarative form, by the novice to take the mental steps that the expert takes automatically and unconsciously. (Britton, Gulgoz, & Glynn, 1992, p. 37)

What should science teachers do if their textbooks are not audience appropriate? At some point, audience-appropriate texts need to be identified and purchased. In the meantime, teachers can offer students alternative texts in the form of information trade books and magazines that focus on the concepts and processes being covered. Although in some cases these resources aren't substitutes for science texts written by qualified experts, often they are clearly written and organized because they are published for the general public.

Notes

Many science tradebook series include reference books on a particular topic, such as types of plants or other organisms; short nature books that explain particular concepts, such as life cycles; publications that focus on a single subject, such as light, magnetism, or electricity; and articles that explain a particular process, such as reproduction (Madrazo, 1997). How can teachers determine whether a trade book is a good choice? Moss, Leone, and DiPillo (1997) suggest that book selections be made on the basis of "five A's":

- *Authority* of the author
- *Accuracy* of text content
- *Appropriateness* of the book for children
- Literary *artistry*
- *Appearance* of the book

Teachers can locate excellent resources on a number of education and science Web sites. For example, the McREL Web site (www.mcrel.org) points visitors to numerous sites that offer suggestions for science resources. Another helpful source for lists of science trade books is *Outstanding Science Trade Books for Children,* published annually by the National Science Teachers Association and the Children's Book Council. Finally, there are a number of questions to consider when selecting textbook passages, articles, and other print material. The list of questions below can serve as a starting point for teachers as they evaluate the text features of students' reading material:

- Are main ideas explicitly stated in prominent locations such as introductions, summaries, headings, or topic sentences?
- Is all information in the text clearly connected to the main idea? Does it contribute to and support the development of this idea?
- Are explanations clear and developmentally appropriate?
- Are concepts thoroughly explained?

- Are ideas written in a logical order (e.g., from first to last, or from most important to least important)?
- Are the relationships between events and ideas clearly stated? Are signal words used to show these relationships?
- Are organizational patterns evident? (Examples of organizational patterns common to science text are explained on pages 21–23 of this supplement.)
- Do the visuals (e.g., graphs, tables, pictures, illustrations, charts) support the author's main ideas? Are they clearly labeled and easily connected to related text? Are they laid out in a way that doesn't distract or confuse the reader?
- Are there advanced organizers to help readers anticipate how information will be organized?

Notes

Section 2

Strategic Processing

Notes

Things to Think About:

1. What kinds of knowledge and skills related to reading science help students succeed in comprehending and learning from science text?
2. What strategies work best for teachers when they personally have trouble comprehending science text?
3. What kinds of questions should teachers ask to determine if students really understood what they read?
4. How can students' writing be used to enhance and extend their learning?

Literacy and learning researchers define metacognition in a number of different ways. In simplest terms, metacognition means thinking about one's thinking. (See Section 2 of the *TRCA Teacher's Manual* for a discussion of metacognition in terms of strategic reading and reflection.) Yore, Shymansky, Henriques, Chidsey, and Lewis (1997) maintain that with regard to science, metacognition encompasses (1) the knowledge the reader has about science text, science reading, and science reading strategies; (2) the skill to read science text and use science reading strategies; and (3) the understanding about why and when to use science reading strategies.

Effective readers of science text demonstrate this knowledge in a number of ways. Exhibit 3 on pages 30–32 is a reprint of what Craig and Yore (1996) describe as "the desired image of an efficient, successful reader of science text material" (p. 230).

Notes

Exhibit 3. The Desired Image of an Efficient, Successful Reader of Science Text Material

Science Reading

1. Realize that science reading is an interactive-constructive process by which they make meaning from personal experience, recorded experiences of other people, and the context of the reading.

2. Develop a sense of the motivation and value for the reading and feel confident that the reading will help to understand, reinforce, and enrich personal experiences, interests, and needs, and to solve problems.

3. Have self-confidence in his/her reading abilities and realize that a comprehension problem may result from poorly written text or abstract ideas, and not just a personal comprehension block.

4. Enjoy science reading and is likely to read science materials outside the prescribed text, and to pursue personal interests in science topics through science reading materials.

5. Monitor successes at understanding the reading information as the reading progresses and detect discrepancies in light of the established purpose, and consciously adopt or determine strategies to review the text information, which help create a better fit between schema and the perceived meaning of the text, carry out these strategies, and reassess the goodness-of-fit for the reviewed textual information and understandings.

6. Adjust comprehension monitoring to more conscious levels when demands of the reading increase, when difficulties are perceived, when conceptual discrepancies are detected, and when comprehension is blocked.

Science Text

7. Realize that words are labels for ideas, ideas are based on experiences, and text is stored descriptions of ideas (experience); that readers must evaluate the textual material; and that readers determine their own purposes for carrying out the reading.

8. Realize that the text is not an absolute truth and that all science writing is a form of interpretation and, at least to some extent, all science writing may be a distortion or simplification of information and ideas that have been developed or recorded through the processes of science.

Exhibit 3 (continued)

Notes

9. Evaluate text passages for plausibility, completeness, and interconnectedness by using available knowledge to detect and correct mistakes in science text writing or to fill in missing information necessary to make the text plausible, or to reorganize and add logical connective to link isolated ideas.

10. Identify a variety of text structures including description, simple listing, chronological ordering, compare-contrast, cause-effect, and problem-solution and select reading strategies appropriate to the text structures encountered.

Science Reading Strategy

11. Select reading strategies appropriate to the needs of the reading process; for example, when the purpose of the reading is to obtain an overview of the text, the student uses skimming, key words, titles and headings, and topic sentences in paragraphs to retrieve the main ideas.

12. Assess his/her own personal skills as a learner and choose strategies for reading the text that fit self-assessment and avoid reading difficult information without access to prior conceptual knowledge (critical vocabulary and key background concepts) or prior strategic knowledge (plans to review and reprocess difficult ideas or concepts).

13. Use visual adjuncts in texts, such as graphs, charts, and photographic reproductions to help clarify, organize, reinforce, enrich, or verify the meanings derived from the text.

14. Use efficient vocabulary development skills to determine the meaning of words from context; to dissect words into prefixes, suffixes and root-words; to utilize classification, concept maps, metaphors, and analogues to show relationships of key words; and to use mnemonic aids to help remember key words.

15. Identify main ideas in a text, delineate supporting ideas, and rephrase ideas to show logical connections and hierarchical relationships explicit or implicit in the text.

16. Summarize text passages using the following macrorules: delete redundancies, delete trivia, provide superordinates, or select topic sentences or invent topic sentences when missing.

Notes

Exhibit 3 (continued)

17. Ask self-questions about the readings that require comprehension and reflect the purpose(s) for reading the textual material.

18. Use inferential and applied comprehension skills to critically synthesize, analyze, evaluate, and apply information regarding fact and opinion, bias, generalizations, causal relationships, and distinctions.

19. Utilize efficient search-ahead and look-back procedures that allow him/her to construct meaning from related or linked information in other parts of the sentence or paragraph.

20. Choose appropriate study skills when there is a need to remember detailed information from text, such as summarizing, outlining, peer testing, and reciprocal teaching.

21. Create organized mental images of information in order to integrate the information into existing schema and to help encode the information into long-term memory.

Note. From "Middle School Students' Awareness of Strategies for Resolving Comprehension Difficulties in Science Reading," by M. T. Craig and L. D. Yore, 1996, *Journal of Research and Development in Education 29*(4), pp. 226–238. Copyright 1996 by the University of Georgia. Reprinted with permission.

In a study of middle school students' awareness and use of metacognitive knowledge, Craig and Yore (1996) found that students neither activated nor used their prior knowledge to make sense of what they read. Students did not read text actively, and the comprehension strategies they resorted to often were limited to re-reading the same passage or asking someone else for help. Although this study represents only one group of students, these findings are not startling. Most students have not been taught the unique aspects of science reading, science text, and science reading strategies. If educators are committed to helping students acquire the level of science literacy they need to succeed in school and in life, then they must equip them with the knowledge and skills they need to read science materials.

Notes

The first step in planning instruction in metacognition is determining what knowledge and skills students already have. Exhibit 4 includes sample questions to ask students in order to discover what they already know about science reading, science text, and science reading strategies. This list is a good place to start when creating one for the classroom.

Exhibit 4. Questions to Ask Students About Reading Strategy Use

1. Before you begin a reading assignment for science, do you leaf through the passage and read the headings to see what the passage is about?
2. Why might it be helpful to think about what you already know about a topic before reading about it?
3. When you have to read something for science, do you make sure you understand the purpose for reading it? What difference would this make?
4. If you thought a topic in your science text was going to be difficult to understand, what could you do before you started reading to help you understand?
5. How is reading in science class different from reading in language arts?
6. Should you stop and think about why you are reading? When should you do this?
7. How do you know if you've really understood a reading assignment for science class?
8. What can you do if you are reading and don't understand what a sentence is about? How would you decide what to do?
9. What do you do when you come to a big word in your science text that you don't know?
10. Are there times when it becomes difficult to understand what you're reading? What makes you realize it is becoming more difficult?

Note. From "Middle School Students' Awareness of Strategies for Resolving Comprehension Difficulties in Science Reading," by M. T. Craig and L. D. Yore, 1996, *Journal of Research and Development in Education 29*(4), pp. 226–238. Copyright 1996 by the University of Georgia. Reprinted with permission.

Notes

After teachers discover what students already know about science reading, science text, and science reading strategies, they can plan instruction. It's important to emphasize that instruction in reading science should be embedded within the context of daily science instruction rather than treated as a separate activity. By embedding reading instruction this way, students can apply each strategy to relevant reading and learning.

One way teachers can introduce science reading strategies is by modeling the think-aloud strategy (see pp. 107–108) for students. Modeling this strategy involves teachers reading aloud a passage from the text and showing students how they monitor their comprehension. For example, teachers might purposely misread something, and then explain how they knew they made an error in reading. They might also demonstrate what they do when they come across something that doesn't make sense or doesn't agree with their beliefs or prior knowledge. It's also useful for teachers to show students how they determine the meaning of a word they are unfamiliar with when they encounter it while reading.

In addition, teachers should model for students how to do ongoing checks for understanding. For example, teachers might show students how they know when they've come to an important concept or main idea. It's also helpful to demonstrate how to continue interacting with the text by mentally self-questioning, summarizing what was read, and thinking about where the content is leading.

Other techniques that can be modeled include forming a mental image of what is being read and adjusting one's reading rate. In addition, we strongly encourage teachers to explain how they know which strategy to use to "fix" a specific comprehension problem. Students may know certain strategies and how to perform them but still not know when or why to select one rather than another.

Once students have learned how to interact with the text to construct meaning, suggest they practice think-alouds with a partner to

increase their understanding of how they process new text. It's important for students to recognize the value of performing these strategies. Struggling readers, in particular, need ongoing reinforcement about the value of using these strategies.

Reflective Questioning

Too often, students don't gain an in-depth understanding of science concepts because the questions they are asked require only literal responses. The QAR strategy (explained on pp. 145–147 of the *TRCA Teacher's Manual* and on pp. 117–119 of this supplement) is a highly effective strategy for helping students think beyond the literal level and apply their new learning in different real-world situations.

Another reason students don't develop an in-depth understanding of what they read is that they resist digging in and grappling with difficult text. Beck, McKeown, Hamilton, and Kucan (1998) developed the Questioning the Author (QtA) strategy to address this problem. They maintain that QtA helps build understanding of text ideas because it requires students to become actively involved as they read, delve more deeply into difficult passages, and grapple with confusing information to make sense of it. QtA is unique because it helps students identify and answer questions they have about text content while reading, rather than waiting until after they have read an entire passage. (See pp. 120–121 for a more complete explanation of this strategy.)

Reflective Writing

Integrating new information into one's knowledge base is an essential part of learning. Writing-to-learn activities and longer writing assignments can help students reflect on what they are learning. These assignments should challenge students to do more than regurgitate definitions or facts. They should require students to explain relationships among ideas and make connections between this information and their past experiences.

Notes

Writing can also provide valuable feedback to students. When students must construct their own explanations for things they observe, they quickly see what they know and don't know. Students' writing can also provide useful feedback to teachers about how students view different ideas, which teachers can use to inform their instruction.

Learning logs are another way for students to reflect on what they know, what they think they will be learning, what they learn, and what still remains confusing. (See pp. 148–150 in the *TRCA Teacher's Manual* and pp. 114–116 in this supplement for science learning log ideas.) Santa and Havens (1991) suggest that teachers introduce learning logs to students by describing this form of writing as writing down their thinking. Reflective writing helps students practice the metacognitive skill of monitoring one's learning.

Tchudi and Huerta (1983) have proposed principles that science teachers can use to guide their use of longer writing-to-learn science tasks. Specifically, teachers should do the following:

- Make sure that all writing tasks focus on science content.
- Help students understand how to organize and synthesize their ideas.
- Develop writing activities that involve students writing for a real audience who will review, question, and critique each student's writing.
- Allow sufficient time for students to prewrite, collect information from a variety of sources, sharpen their focus, and plan their writing.
- Provide ongoing support and instruction as students make revisions to their writing based on the feedback they receive.
- Help students recognize the differences between rewriting and editing what they write (i.e., in terms of spelling, grammar, and mechanics).

These principles support the research on the effective use of writing-to-learn. Writing is best viewed as a process rather than a product. In the science classroom, writing assignments should engage students in reflecting on authentic science situations and writing for specific, "real-life" audiences who may not be familiar with the topic, rather than writing for an expert — their teacher.

Anthony, Johnson, and Yore (1996) note that one problem science teachers often confront when they assign writing tasks is that students merely copy text material into their assignments without "digesting" or summarizing these ideas and making them their own. Anthony et al. suggest three reasons that students don't reflect on and learn from writing: (1) the resource text material is already framed or organized in the required format; (2) students are taking this material, written by experts, and turning it in to the teacher who is an informed audience rather than one that needs more extensive explanation; and (3) the writing isn't focused on authentic questions that require students to synthesize ideas into unifying concepts. Therefore, it is essential that writing assignments be constructed as learning assignments in which students wrestle with their own real-life applications of concepts and processes learned in class.

Teachers who want students to use resource materials to support their writing can facilitate this by requiring students to gather information from a number of different resources — magazines, journals, trade books, videos, and the Internet. It's also helpful to designate one area of the classroom for writing and another as the resource area, which should include a variety of materials. Use the "separation rule" by telling students that they can have at their desks either a resource book or their notebook, but not both. This system has been used effectively even with young students. It encourages students to digest larger amounts of information and then to summarize this information in writing, while discouraging reading solely for recall of one-word bits of information that students race to their desks to write down (Anthony, Johnson, & Yore, 1996). Novice

Notes

Notes

readers will need the requisite instruction in summarizing prior to working independently on summarizing assignments (see group summarizing on page 87).

Section 3

Strategic Teaching

Notes

Things to Think About:

1. What is science literacy?
2. What components of science instruction help students become science literate?
3. What are the potential obstacles to science literacy in K–12 education and what can be done to address them?

Strategic teaching means being purposeful and thoughtful about planning instruction. It means identifying a learning goal, considering students' knowledge and needs, and then selecting appropriate instructional strategies.

As described by the *National Science Education Standards* (NRC, 1996), the goal of science education is for all students to "achieve scientific literacy" (p. ix). Achieving literacy in science is defined as "the knowledge and understanding of scientific concepts and processes required for personal decision making, participation in civic and cultural affairs, and economic productivity. It also includes specific types of abilities" (NRC, p. 22).

Because of time constraints and a crowded science syllabus, the goal often becomes covering material rather than helping students construct meaning. But science literacy cannot be achieved through an accumulation of facts, vocabulary, and fun activities that have no obvious connection to learning key content. In classrooms where science literacy is the goal, teachers plan learning experiences that help students construct meaning rather than simply complete tasks. These teachers schedule time for students to explore, make observations, take wrong turns, test ideas, and do things over. They also plan time for students to calibrate instruments, collect samples, and construct physical and mathematical models. Furthermore, these teachers understand that students need time to learn whatever

Notes

mathematics, technology, and science they need to deal with the questions at hand; time to ask questions, read, and argue; time to wrestle with unfamiliar ideas; and time to see the advantage in thinking differently (Nelson, 1999).

Instructional models are designed to help teachers plan, organize, and sequence learning experiences that help students construct meaning. Common components that are shared by science instructional models include the following five phases (see NRC, 2000):

- **Phase 1:** Students *engage* with a scientific question, event, or phenomenon. This helps them make connections to their prior knowledge and experience. It also causes them to confront the ways in which their prior knowledge may not align with these new ideas, which can motivate students to learn more.
- **Phase 2:** Students *explore* ideas through hands-on experiences. They also formulate and test hypotheses and solve problems. During their exploration, students create explanations for what they observe.
- **Phase 3:** Students *explain* what they have learned by analyzing and interpreting data, synthesizing their ideas, and building models. During this important phase, students can clarify their understanding of concepts and explanations by consulting with their teachers and other sources of scientific knowledge.
- **Phase 4:** Students *elaborate* their new understanding and skills, applying what they have learned to new situations and circumstances.
- **Phase 5:** With their teachers, students review and *evaluate* what they have learned and how they have learned it.

Obstacles to Effective Science Learning

Many obstacles lie in the way of all students becoming science literate. Among these are curricula and textbooks that attempt to

Notes

cover too much content. Teachers often feel obligated to cover everything in a book, resulting in a "mile-wide and inch-deep" curriculum.

Even teachers who plan lessons around the five-phase instructional model sometimes find themselves ending lessons at the *exploration* phase because of lack of time or expertise in guiding students through the remaining phases. However, eliminating opportunities for students to *explain*, *elaborate*, and *evaluate* diminishes opportunities for them to construct meaning.

Moreover, students who don't have opportunities to wrestle with new ideas aren't likely to revise misconceptions they may hold about scientific phenomena. Roth (1991) asserts that students who have constructed their own inaccurate theories have to go through a difficult process of conceptual change, a process that takes time, focused instruction, and follow-through.

As a classroom teacher and researcher, Roth grew frustrated with science textbooks and students' failure to learn from them. When students did not delve deeply into text, they failed to recognize conceptual conflicts between their prior knowledge and text explanations that would help them revise their incorrect theories. Based on conceptual change research and her own observations as an educator, Roth developed a set of guidelines for using textbooks to promote conceptual change.

Guidelines for Promoting Conceptual Change

This supplement does not champion any one model of planning instruction. Nevertheless, because Roth's (1991) guidelines for initiating conceptual change align well with the five phases of instruction described earlier, we discuss these ideas briefly here. Roth contends that to promote conceptual change, science teachers should do the following:

Notes

- *Focus on a few critical issues rather than trying to cover all the content in a textbook.* Roth recommends that teachers identify central concepts in the text that are most likely to conflict with students' personal theories and define a central question or problem that students' reading assignments and hands-on activities will help answer.
- *Ask questions that challenge students' beliefs and that force them to see how their understanding differs from the text.* Typically, unless learners are forced to confront their misconceptions, they ignore information that conflicts with their beliefs — or distort it to make it fit their personal theories. Phases 1 and 2 of instruction (*engagement* and *exploration*) are likely times to introduce conceptual conflict, although challenging students' thinking can be useful during all phases of instruction.
- *Plan activities that create a sense of disequilibrium in students regarding the troublesome concepts.* Roth explains that when students engage in activities or experiments that bring them face to face with evidence that contradicts their own theories, they are more easily convinced that there may be better explanations for phenomena. Whole-class and small group discussions that accompany these activities are an essential part of the conceptual change process. These discussions support Phase 3 activities; as students reflect on and *explain* any conceptual conflict they are experiencing, teachers can help them construct meaning from the activities and restructure their schema to reflect their new understanding.
- *Present text explanations in a variety of different ways.* Typically, students read text material during Phase 3 of the instructional process. Roth cautions that science textbooks often explain a concept in only one way before moving on to explain other, related concepts. As a result, students don't have time to make meaningful sense of what they are learning. Roth argues that teachers "must give students time to grapple with these explanations … [and] help students recognize ways in which the text explanations differ from their own views" (p. 59). She

also recommends that teachers explain concepts discussed in the text in a number of different ways so that students have a greater chance of recognizing and resolving conceptual conflicts.

- *Provide several opportunities for students to apply text concepts to everyday phenomena.* As described in Phase 4, it is essential that students elaborate their knowledge by applying what they have learned to new situations. This reinforces students' new understanding.

Exhibit 5 on page 44 highlights Roth's views on common, troublesome aspects of science text, difficulties these cause student readers, and ways to tackle these problems using her instructional guidelines for conceptual change.

At this point, we suggest that readers of this supplement take a moment to review the levels and kinds of strategic reading instruction they provide for their students. Our experience has shown that although some teachers think they are *teaching* reading comprehension, in fact they are *assessing* students' comprehension. Strategic teaching must include explaining to students *how* to read science text. It should support and guide students during the process of reading text and other resource material and offer constructive feedback as the lesson proceeds. For example, when instructing students about how to identify the main idea of a passage, teachers should share with students not only how they, as readers themselves, find a main idea but also *how they know* it is the main idea.

In summary, strategic teaching means being purposeful and thoughtful about planning instruction. Teachers should choose strategies that are best suited to their content and their individual students. Instruction in reading strategies should include time for modeling, guided practice, independent practice, and application. Students equipped with multiple tools and strategies are more likely to have meaningful, interesting, challenging, and successful science experiences.

Notes

Exhibit 5. Principles for Promoting Conceptual Change Learning From Text

Common Troublesome Features of Science Textbooks	Resulting Student Difficulties	Ways of Overcoming the Problem and Promoting Conceptual Change Learning
Content coverage is broad and shallow, with emphasis on specialized vocabulary words. Many concepts are covered, but they are addressed superficially, not in ways that promote real understanding.	Encourages students to approach learning science as memorizing lists of unrelated facts and vocabulary words.	Focus on a few critical issues.
Science textbooks are written from scientists' perspectives and do not seriously consider students' ways of thinking.	Students fail to change their ideas, either because they do not see the connections between their own ideas and those in the text or because they distort the text to make it fit their prior knowledge.	Ask questions to elicit and challenge students' thinking and misconceptions.
Teacher's guides for textbooks give correct answers to questions without anticipating or discussing alternative student responses.	Students develop inappropriate strategies for getting right answers and continue to hold critical misunderstandings. They view learning science as a process of getting right answers, even if the answers don't make sense to them.	Probe student responses and give students clear feedback about their ideas.
Explanations of concepts are given in only one way, and explanations of related concepts come in rapid succession.	Students holding different views cannot link the text explanation to their own ideas. They see text explanations as things to be memorized that have nothing to do with their own understandings of the world.	Represent text explanations in different ways that make explicit the contrast and connections between scientific concepts and students' misconceptions.
Activities/experiments are optional supplements that are not closely linked to concepts presented in the text.	Students learn that doing science has little to do with reading and thinking about science concepts and that text ideas are separate from the real world. Activities are fun for students but don't help them develop better understandings of concepts.	Select activities to create conceptual conflict and to develop conceptual understanding.
Questions posed to students in textbooks are primarily fact oriented; they rarely require students to construct explanations.	Students think they understand science because they can answer fact questions, but they may continue to hold critical misconceptions that have not been challenged.	Ask questions that give students repeated opportunities to apply text concepts to explain real world phenomena.

Note. From *Science Learning: Processes and Applications* (p. 57), by C. M. Santa and D. E. Alvermann (Eds.), 1991, Newark, DE: International Reading Association. Reprinted with permission of Carol M. Santa and the International Reading Association.

Section 4

Six Assumptions About Learning

Six Assumptions About Learning

Learning is:

1. Goal-oriented
2. The linking of new information to prior knowledge
3. The organization of information
4. The acquisition of cognitive and metacognitive structures
5. Nonlinear, yet occurring in phases
6. Influenced by cognitive development

Recent research about student learning emphasizes learning for understanding. This research provides insights that can strengthen the link between what researchers know about learning and what happens in the classroom.

Jones, Palincsar, Ogle, and Carr (1987) have proposed six assumptions about how students learn. Because these assumptions stem from significant research and have important implications for reading, including reading in science, they warrant study by educators who want to examine how learning theory aligns with and undergirds reading theory. (These assumptions are discussed in more depth in Section 4 of the *TRCA Teacher's Manual,* pp. 61–67.)

Assumption 1: Learning is goal oriented.

Skilled learners have two goals: to construct meaning and to regulate learning. Reading is not a passive activity; it is the active construction of meaning by learners. Both inquiry and reading should involve the processes of planning, monitoring, evaluating comprehension, making inferences, drawing conclusions, revising schema, extending and refining knowledge, and analyzing information based on prior knowledge. These processes help learners construct meaning and regulate their learning. Simply doing a "cookbook" science activity or engaging in reading as merely a word-calling exercise does not help students construct meaning or regulate their learning.

Notes

Notes

Assumption 2: Learning is the linking of new information to prior knowledge.

Students bring to a learning experience their current explanations, attitudes, and abilities. They have conceptions and misconceptions about the natural world, both of which influence their learning. Through meaningful interactions with their environment, with their teachers, and among themselves, they reorganize, redefine, and replace their initial explanations, attitudes, and abilities (NRC, 2000). Textbooks, however, are often set up in a "tell-and-verify" format; students are expected to read about science and then do a cookbook experiment that verifies what they have just read. Providing students with the opportunity to explore science concepts through stimulating, hands-on activities and investigations *before* reading can give students the opportunity to have concepts reinforced, confirmed, or enriched as they read about them.

Assumption 3: Learning involves organizing information.

Realizing that authors of informational science text (textbooks or trade books) organize information in a variety of organizational patterns can help learners make meaning of what they have read. Similarly, helping students make connections between the science activities they are doing and their science reading can aid their understanding of science concepts.

Assumption 4: Learning is the acquisition of cognitive and metacognitive structures.

Strategic learners are aware of their learning styles and are able to select and regulate their use of learning skills and strategies. Strategic processing is discussed more fully in Section 2 of this supplement (see pp. 29–38).

Assumption 5: Learning occurs in phases, yet is nonlinear.

Costa and Garmston (1994) and Buehl (1995) believe that learning has three phases: preactive thought, interactive thought, and reflective thought. Preactive thought involves preparing for learning;

interactive thought (or processing) occurs during learning; and reflective thought involves integrating, extending, refining, and applying what has been learned. Strategies found in Section 5 of this supplement are identified by the appropriate phase.

Assumption 6: Learning is influenced by cognitive development. Not all students arrive at school with the same set of knowledge and skills. Effective readers may have their own reading strategies; other readers may benefit from learning additional reading strategies; and poor readers may not be aware that there are strategies to help with understanding.

The following section of this supplement is a toolkit of strategies designed to increase students' conceptual understanding of science. Strategies are classified as vocabulary development, informational text, and reflection strategies. They are also identified as *preactive* (preparation before reading), *interactive* (assistance during reading), and/or *reflective* (reflection after reading).

Notes

Section 5
Reading Strategies

Strategies for the Three Phases of Cognitive Processing		Proactive Preparation Before Reading	Interactive Assistance During Reading	Reflective Reflection After Reading
Vocabulary Development	**Page Number**			
S-1 Concept Definition Mapping	50	x	x	x
S-2 Frayer Model	53	x	x	x
S-3 Semantic Feature Analysis	58	x	x	x
S-4 Semantic Mapping	61	x	x	x
S-5 Student VOC Strategy	64	x	x	
S-6 Word Sort	69	x	x	x
Informational Text				
S-7 Anticipation Guide/Revised Extended Anticipation Guide	72	x	x	x
S-8 Directed Reading/Thinking Activity (DR/TA)	76	x	x	x
S-9 Graphic Organizer	81	x	x	x
S-10 Group Summarizing	87			x
S-11 What I Know; Want to Learn; Learned (K-W-L)	91	x		x
S-12 Pairs Read	94		x	
S-13 Predict; Locate; Add; Note (PLAN)	95	x	x	x
S-14 Problematic Situation	99	x		x
S-15 Proposition/Support Outline	101		x	x
S-16 Reciprocal Teaching	105	x	x	x
S-17 Survey, Question, Read, Recite, Review (SQ3R)	106	x	x	x
S-18 Think-Aloud	107		x	
Reflection Strategies (Questioning; Writing; Discussing)				
S-19 Creative Debate	109			x
S-20 Discussion Web	111			x
S-21 Learning Log	114	x	x	x
S-22 Question-Answer Relationship (QAR)	117			x
S-23 Questioning the Author (QtA)	120		x	x
S-24 Role/Audience/Format/Topic (RAFT)	122			x
S-25 Scored Discussion	124			x

Notes

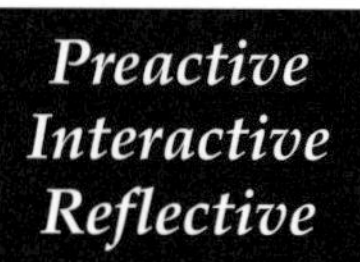

Vocabulary Development

S-1. Concept Definition Mapping

What is it?

Concept definition mapping (Schwartz, 1988) is a strategy for teaching students the meaning of key concepts. Concept definition maps are graphic organizers that help students understand the essential attributes, qualities, or characteristics of a word's meaning. Students must describe what the concept is, make comparisons, tell what it is like, and cite examples of it.

How could it be used in science instruction?

This strategy provides a structure for students to organize their understanding after they have completed an activity and/or read about a concept. It gives students an opportunity to *explain* their understanding and to *elaborate* by citing examples from their own experiences.

How to use it:

1. Display an example of a concept definition map.
2. Discuss the questions that a definition should answer:
   - What is it? What broader category does it fit into?
   - What can it be compared/contrasted to?
   - What is it like? What are its essential characteristics? What qualities make it different from other things in the same category?
   - What are some examples of it?
3. Model how to use the map.
4. Provide students with time to practice.
5. Instruct students to use the information from their maps to write a complete definition of the concept.
6. As a unit progresses, encourage students to refine their maps and to reflect on their learning.

For further discussion of this strategy, see the *TRCA Teacher's Manual*, pp. 70–73.

Vocabulary Development

Notes

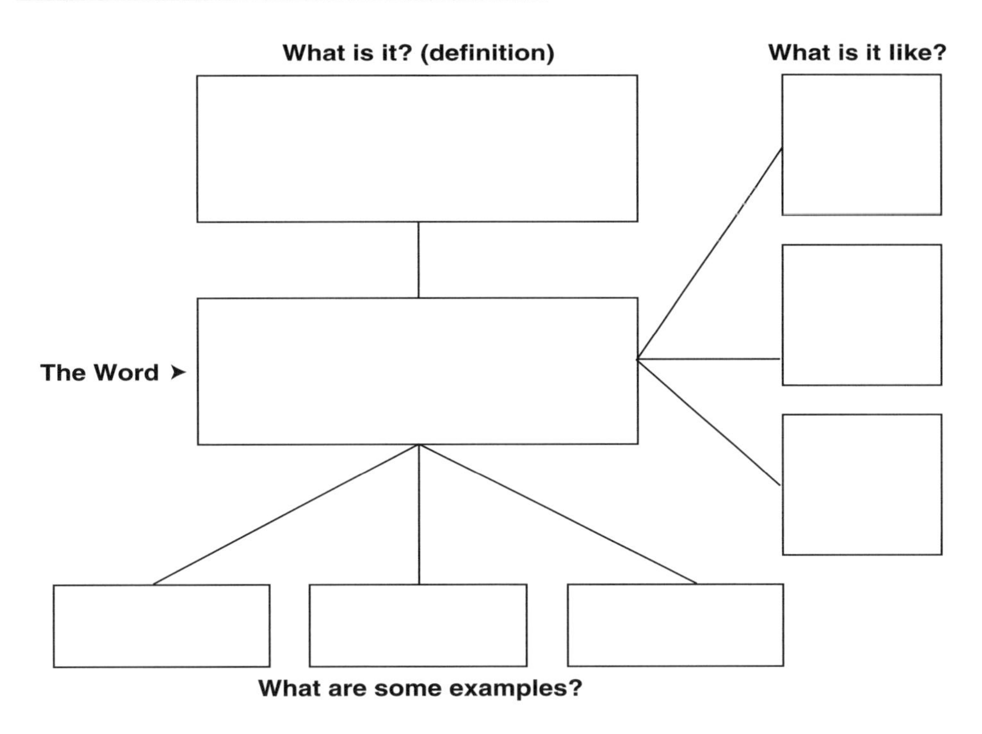

Note. From "Concept of Definition: A Key to Improving Students' Vocabulary," by R. M. Schwartz and T. E. Raphael, 1985, *The Reading Teacher, 39*(2). Reprinted with permission of Taffy E. Raphael and the International Reading Association.

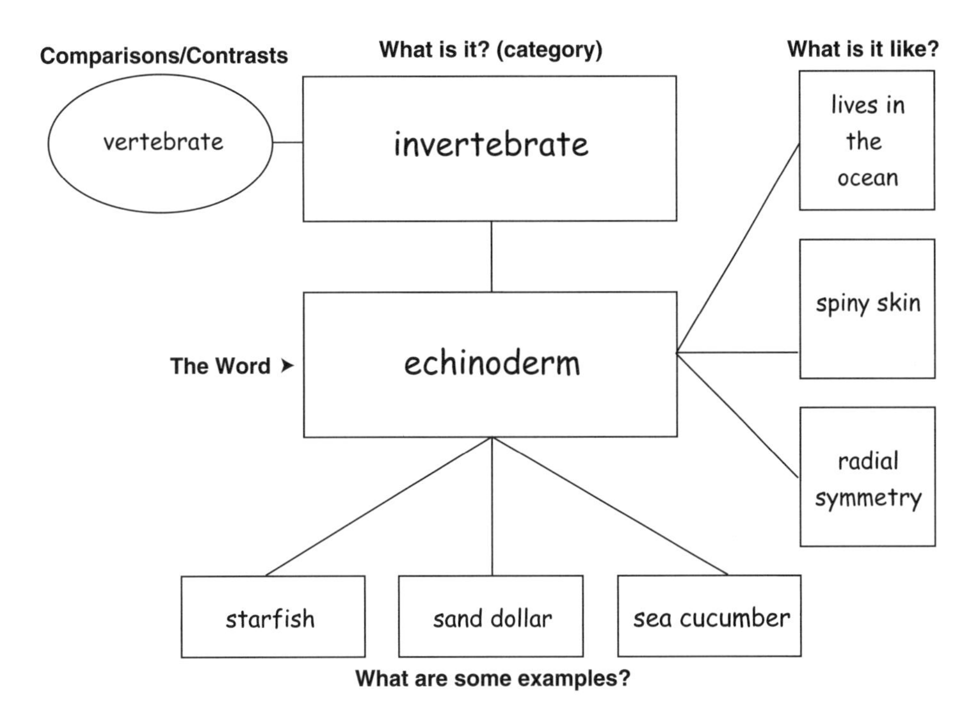

Note. Basic format only from "Concept of Definition: A Key to Improving Students' Vocabulary," by R. M. Schwartz and T. E. Raphael, 1985, *The Reading Teacher, 39*(2).

Notes

Vocabulary Development

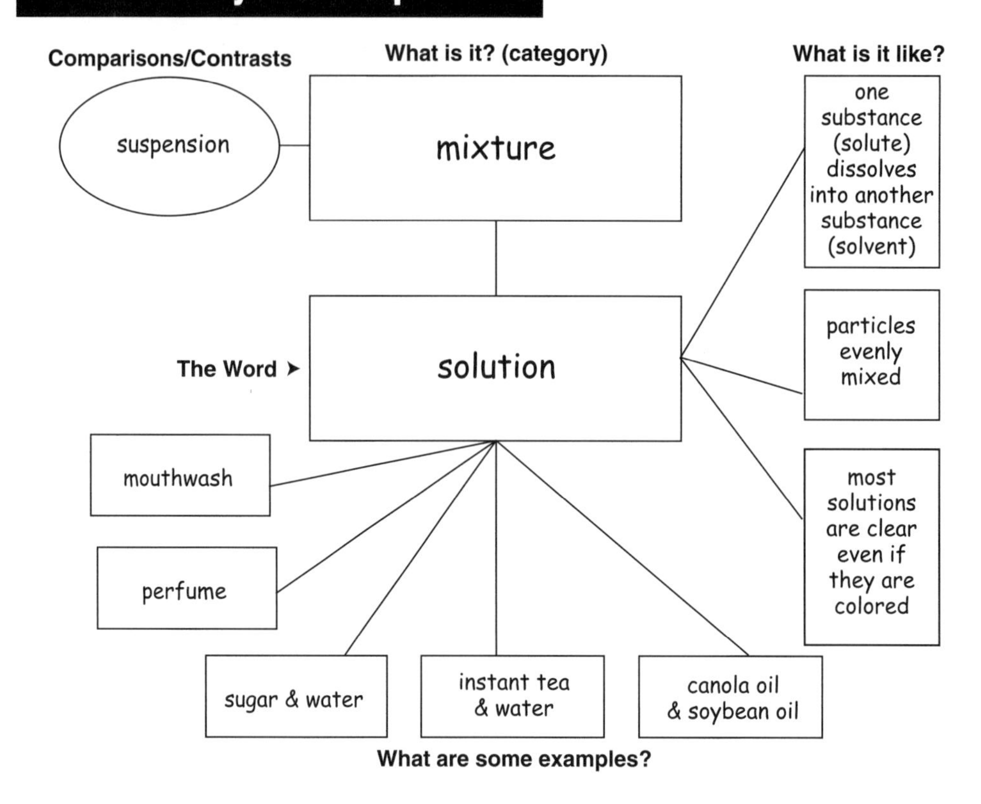

Note. Basic format only from "Concept of Definition: A Key to Improving Students' Vocabulary," by R. M. Schwartz and T. E. Raphael, 1985, *The Reading Teacher, 39*(2). Copyright 1985 by the International Reading Association.

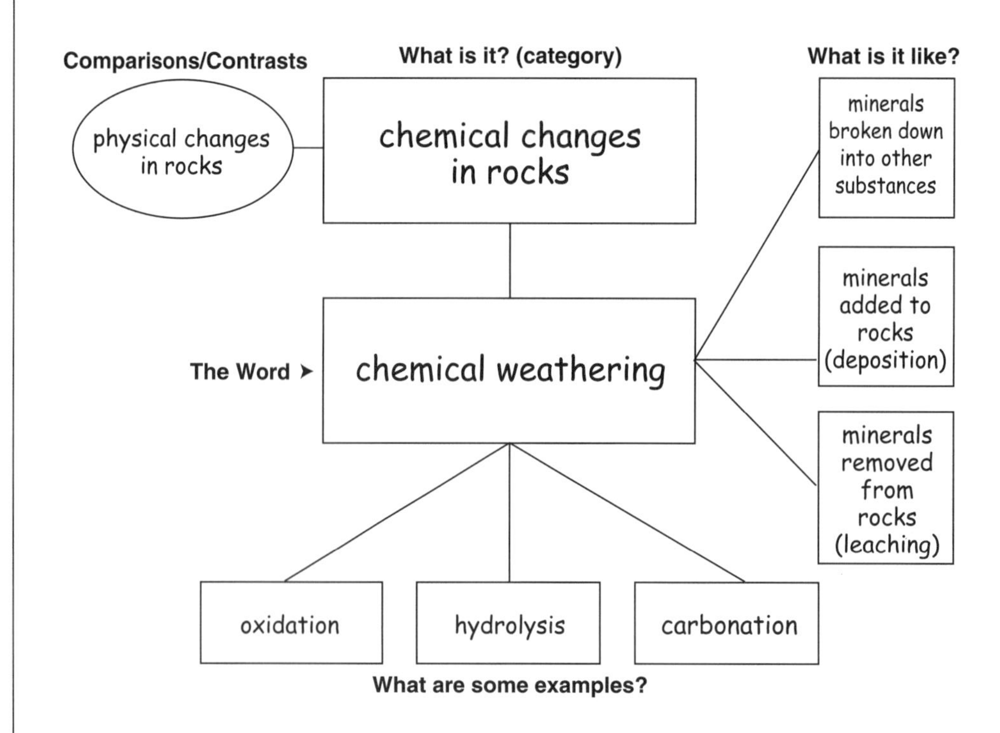

Note. Basic format only from "Concept of Definition: A Key to Improving Students' Vocabulary," by R. M. Schwartz and T. E. Raphael, 1985, *The Reading Teacher, 39*(2). Copyright 1985 by the International Reading Association.

Vocabulary Development

Preactive
Interactive
Reflective

S-2. Frayer Model

Notes

What is it?

The Frayer model (Frayer, Frederick, & Klausmeier, 1969) is a word categorization activity that helps learners to develop their understanding of concepts. Two versions of the Frayer model are included in this manual. In the first, students provide a definition, list characteristics, and provide examples and nonexamples of the concept. In the second, students analyze a word's essential and nonessential characteristics and refine their understanding by choosing examples and nonexamples of the concept.

How could it be used in science instruction?

There are many concepts in science that can be confusing because of their close relationships (e.g., physical change/chemical change). This strategy provides students with the opportunity to understand what a concept is and what it is not. It gives students an opportunity to *explain* their understanding and to *elaborate* by providing examples and nonexamples from their own lives.

How to use it:

1. Assign a concept that might be confusing because of its relational qualities.
2. Explain the Frayer model diagram.
3. Model how to fill out the diagram.
4. Provide students with time to practice with assigned terms.
5. Once the diagram is complete, let students share their work with other students. Display students' diagrams as posters throughout the unit so students can refer to the words and continue to add ideas.

For further discussion of this strategy, see the *TRCA Teacher's Manual*, pp. 74–77.

Notes

Vocabulary Development

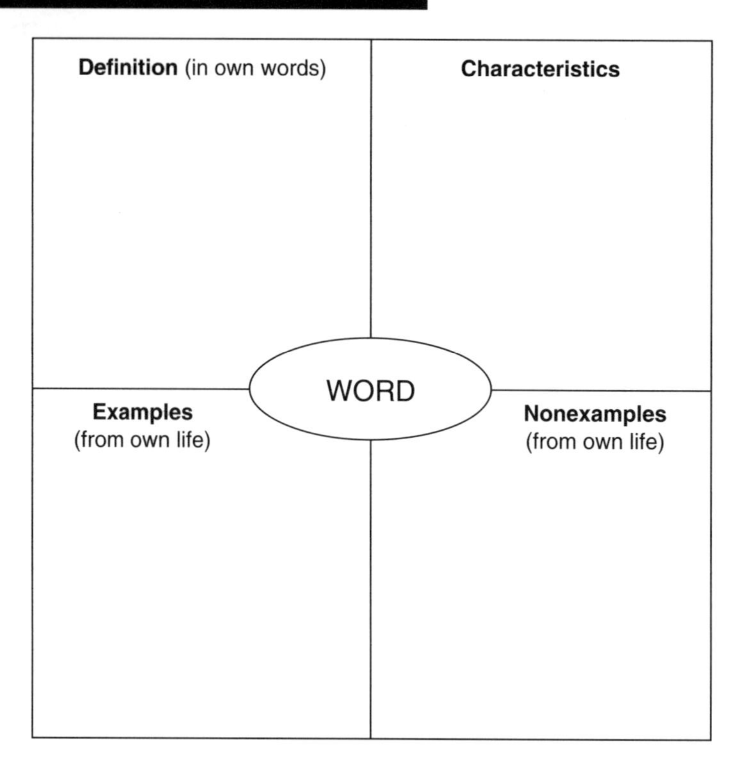

Note. From "A Schema for Testing the Level of Concept Mastery," by D. A. Frayer, W. C. Frederick, and H. G. Klausmeier, in *Technical Report No. 16*. Copyright 1969 by the University of Wisconsin. Reprinted with permission.

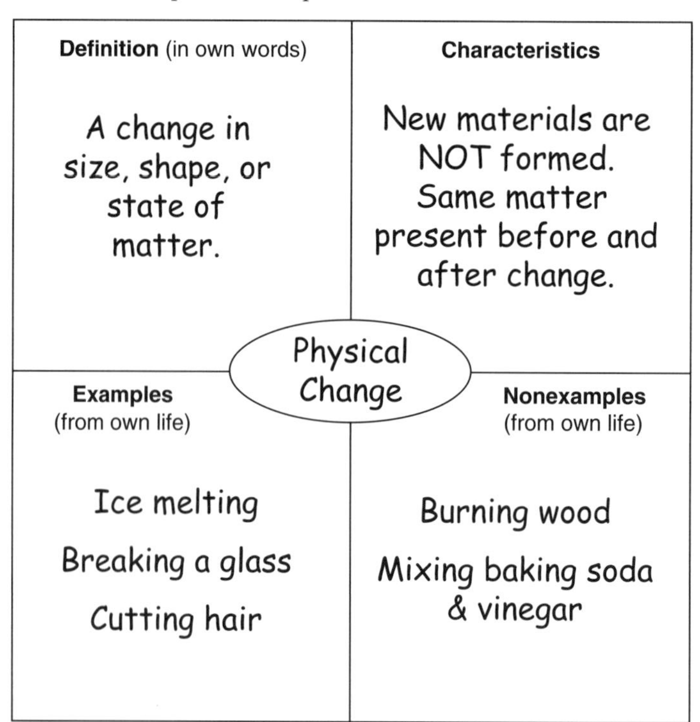

Note. Basic format only from "A Schema for Testing the Level of Concept Mastery," by D. A. Frayer, W. C. Frederick, and H. G. Klausmeier, in *Technical Report No. 16*. Copyright 1969 by the University of Wisconsin.

Vocabulary Development

Definition (in own words)	**Characteristics**
Directed against all infections, regardless of the cause	Not directed against a particular pathogen
Examples (from own life)	**Nonexamples** (from own life)
Skin, Sweat, Mucus, Tears, Cilia, Saliva, White blood cells, Interferons	Antibodies, Vaccines, T-Cells

Nonspecific Immune System Defenses

Note. Basic format only from "A Schema for Testing the Level of Concept Mastery," by D. A. Frayer. W. C. Frederick, and H. G. Klausmeier, in *Technical Report No. 16*. Copyright 1969 by the University of Wisconsin.

Notes

Vocabulary Development

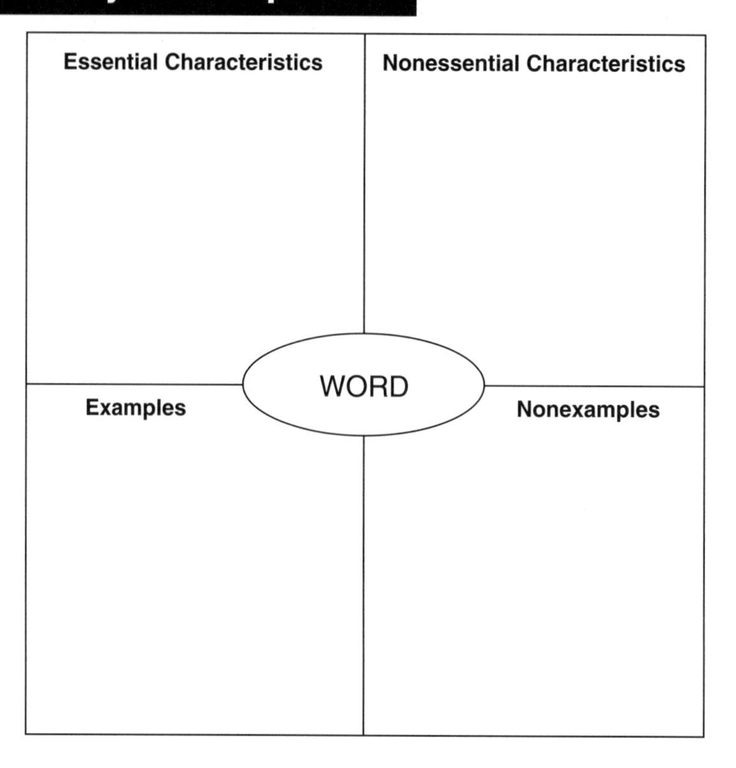

Note. From "A Schema for Testing the Level of Concept Mastery," by D. A. Frayer, W. C. Frederick, and H. G. Klausmeier, in *Technical Report No. 16*. Copyright 1969 by the University of Wisconsin. Reprinted with permission.

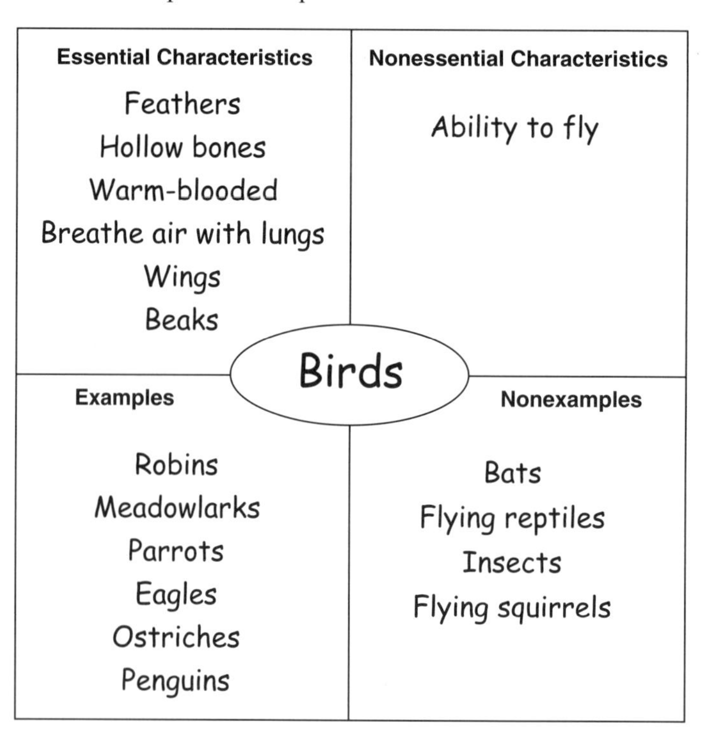

Note. Basic format only from "A Schema for Testing the Level of Concept Mastery," by D. A. Frayer, W. C. Frederick, and H. G. Klausmeier, in *Technical Report No. 16*. Copyright 1969 by the University of Wisconsin.

Vocabulary Development

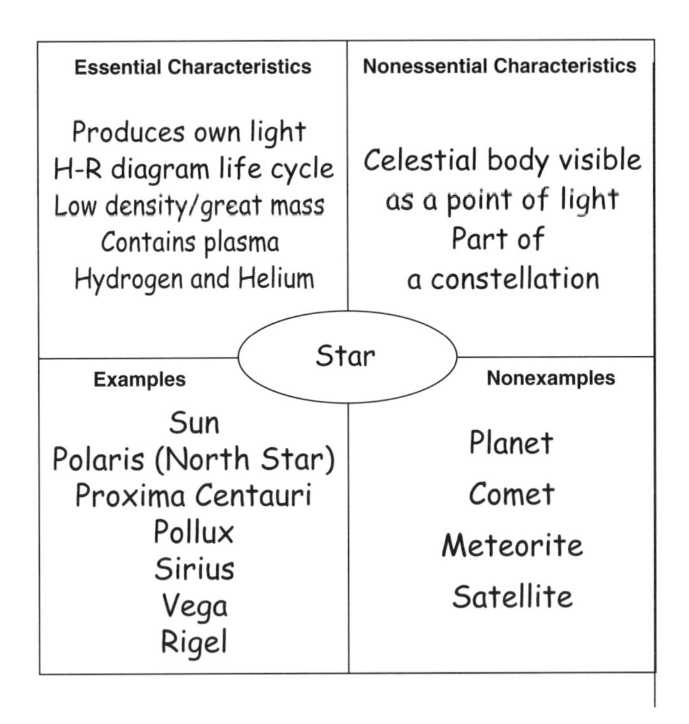

Note. Basic format only from "A Schema for Testing the Level of Concept Mastery," by D. A. Frayer, W. C. Frederick, and H. G. Klausmeier, in *Technical Report No. 16*. Copyright 1969 by the University of Wisconsin.

Notes

Notes

Vocabulary Development

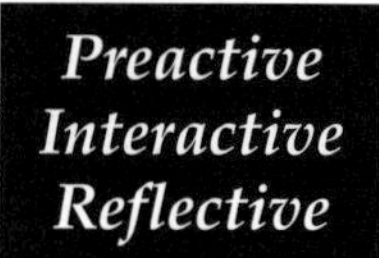

S-3. Semantic Feature Analysis

What is it?

Semantic feature analysis (Baldwin, Ford, & Readence, 1981; Johnson & Pearson, 1984) helps students discern a term's meaning by comparing its features to those of other terms that fall into the same category. When students have completed a semantic feature matrix, they have a visual reminder of how certain terms are alike or different.

How could it be used in science instruction?

This strategy is very effective when examining discriminating features (e.g., categorizing vertebrates, invertebrates, types of rocks, powders, and crystals). This strategy can be used to *engage* student thinking, as a way to collect data while students *explore* similarities and differences, or as a way to quickly *evaluate* students' knowledge.

How to use it:

1. Select a general category of study.
2. Create a matrix. Along the left side, list key terms in the chosen category. Across the top of the matrix, write features that these words might share.
3. Ask students to then use an "X" to indicate if the feature applies to the word or write in specifics about the features.
4. Encourage students to *explain* the rationale behind their choices.
5. As the unit progresses and understanding of each term or concept deepens, the teacher or students can add terms and features to the matrix.

For further discussion of this strategy, see the *TRCA Teacher's Manual*, pp. 79–81.

Notes

Semantic Feature Analysis Grid

Category:

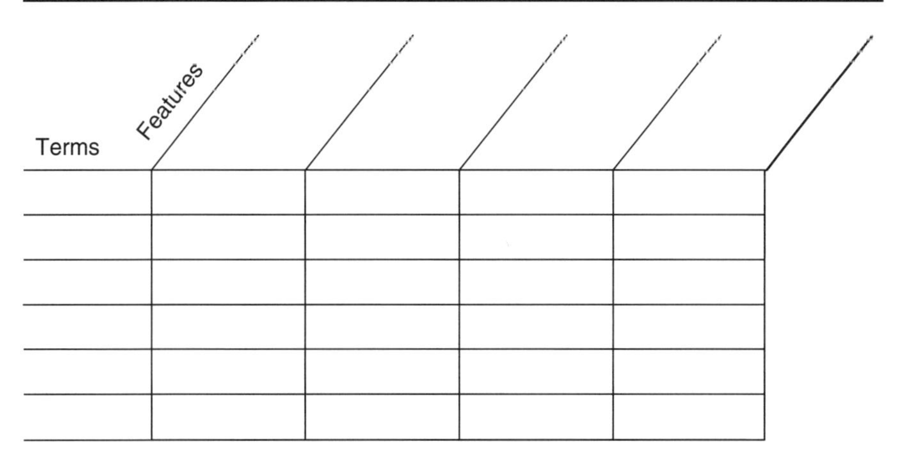

Category: Vertebrates

Terms \ Features	backbone	cold-blooded	warm-blooded	gills	lungs	smooth skin	scales	feathers	fur or hair	produce milk for young
fish	X	X		X			X			
amphibian	X	X		X	X	X				
reptile	X	X			X		X			
bird	X		X		X			X		
mammal	X		X		X				X	X

Notes

Vocabulary Development

Category: Rocks

Terms / Features	dull	shiny	soft	hard	porous	one color	many colors
sandstone	X		sometimes	sometimes	sometimes		X
shale	X		X			X	
obsidian		X		X		X	
pumice	X			X	X	X	
marble		X		X		mainly	
quartzite		X		X			X

Category: Waves

Terms / Features	wavelengths	frequencies (Hz)	detected by	transfer
radiowaves	>1mm	$1–10^8$	radios	radiation
microwaves	1 m–30 cm	$10^8–10^{12}$	microwave detectors	radiation
heat	2.5 m–25 m	$10^{11}–10^{12}$	thermometer	conduction, convection, radiation
light	400nm–750nm	$4x10^{14}–7.5x10^{14}$	eyes	radiation
X-rays	1pm–1nm	$10^{17}–10^{20}$	X-ray film	radiation
sound	1.5cm–16.5m	20–20,000	ears	vibration

Preactive
Interactive
Reflective

Notes

S-4. Semantic Mapping

What is it?

A semantic map is a visual tool that helps readers activate and draw on prior knowledge, recognize important components of different concepts, and see the relationships among these components.

How could it be used in science instruction?

This strategy can be incorporated into the *engagement* phase of a lesson and used throughout a science unit. Students will be able to visualize how terms are connected and/or related. This strategy *engages* students' prior knowledge and can be used to build connections between hands-on activities and reading activities.

How to use it:

1. Write the major concept of the lesson or unit on chart paper.
2. Instruct students to brainstorm a list of terms that relate in some way to the major concept.
3. Write the major concept in the center of another sheet of chart paper and circle it.
4. Encourage students to review the brainstormed list and begin to categorize the terms. The categories and terms should be discussed and then displayed in the form of a map or web.
5. Leave the chart up throughout the lesson or unit so that new categories and terms can be added as needed.

For further discussion of this strategy, see the *TRCA Teacher's Manual*, pp. 82–84.

Notes

Vocabulary Development

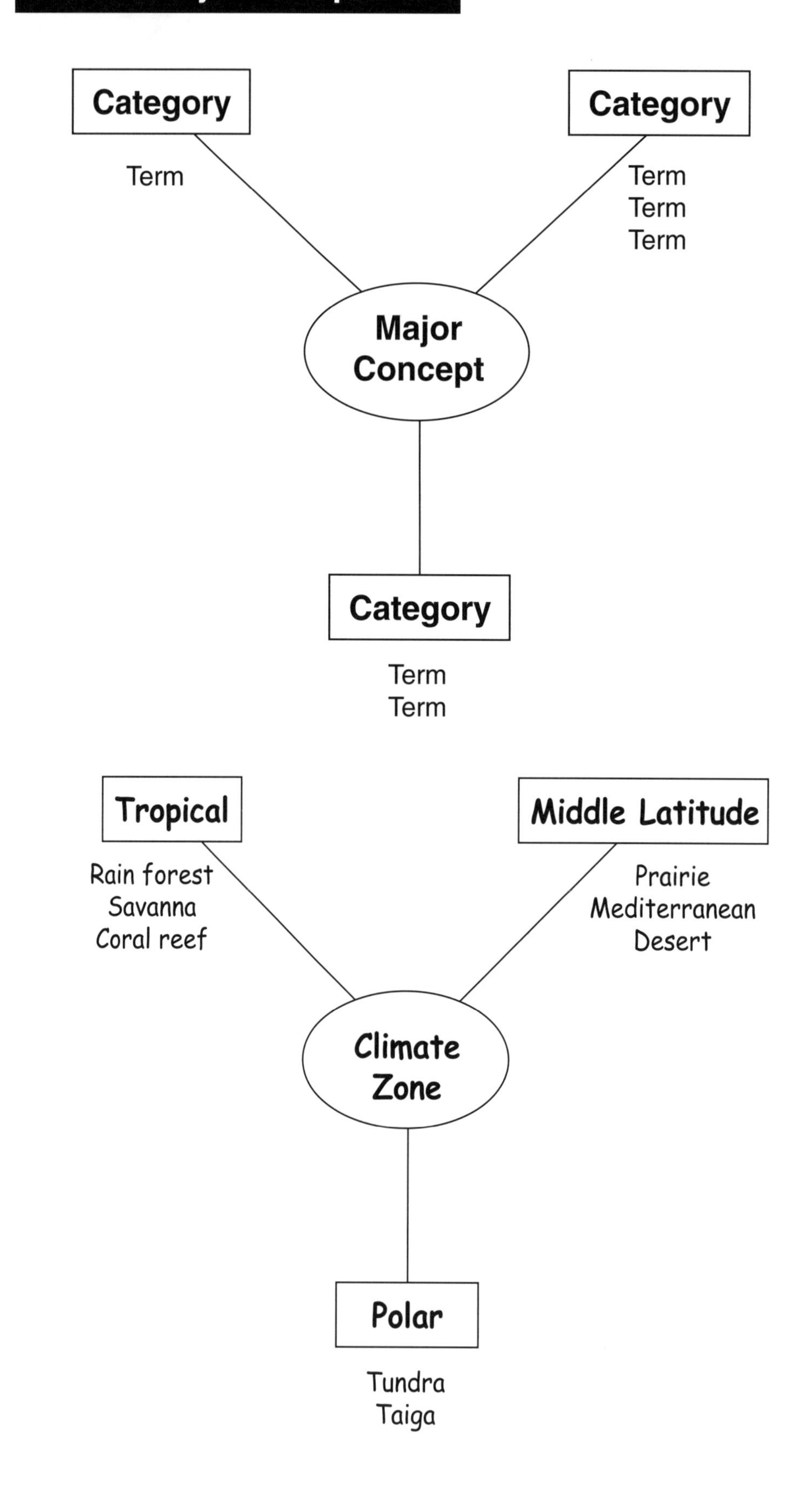

Vocabulary Development

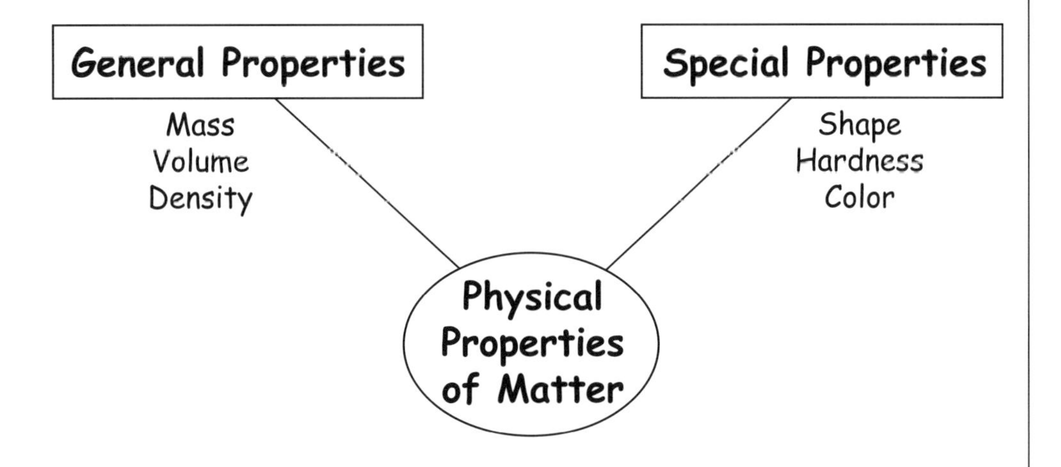

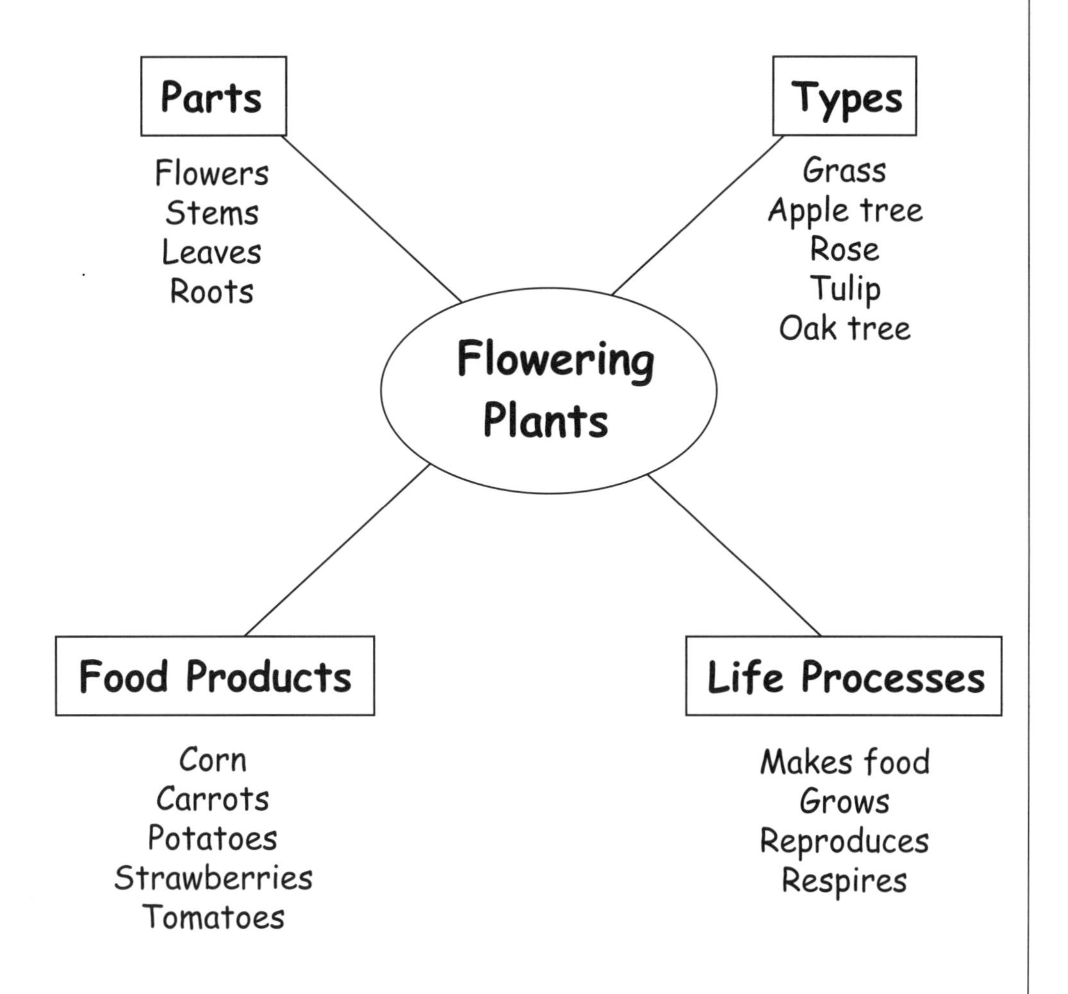

Notes

Notes

Vocabulary Development

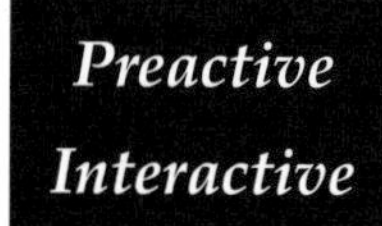

S-5. Student VOC Strategy

What is it?

The student VOC strategy is useful for helping students analyze word meanings from context. The strategy also allows students to make meaningful sensory connections that relate to their particular learning style. When students write their definition for a term and then make a sensory connection with it, they are engaged in a "whole" brain activity that increases retention.

How could it be used in science instruction?

This strategy can be incorporated while students are *exploring* through reading. It is helpful when students might not be able to understand a term from context alone.

How to use it:

1. Assign a passage for students to read.
2. Share key vocabulary words with students prior to reading.
3. Direct students to identify unfamiliar terms on the list and to learn their meanings by using the VOC strategy (see form on page 65) either before reading the passage or while reading it.
4. Encourage students to share their strategies for remembering a word's meaning.

This strategy can be streamlined by asking students to simply draw a picture and write a brief explanation of a term to illustrate understanding. It can also be expanded to include opportunities to write a poem, do a skit, or make up a song about a term.

For further discussion of this strategy, see the *TRCA Teacher's Manual*, pp. 87–88.

Notes

Student VOC Strategy

Vocabulary Word: ______________________________

1. Write the sentence in which it appears in the text:

____

____

2. Based upon how it is used in the text, predict what the word means:

____

3. Consult an "expert" for the actual definition (e.g., a friend, teacher, text resource). Expert: ______________________________

Expert's definition: ______________________________

____

____

4. Show your understanding of the word by using it in a sentence of your own: ______________________________

____

____

5. Choose one of the following ways to help you remember the word's meaning: draw a picture of what the word means to you; select and perform a miming action that the word reminds you of; or connect the word with something similar that you've heard — in a story, a news report, or a song. Write down an association or connection you have made: ______________________________

____

6. Explain why you chose this way to represent what the word means to you:

____

____

Notes

Vocabulary Development

Student VOC Strategy

Vocabulary Word: indirect evidence

1. Write the sentence in which it appears in the text: Indirect evidence is a set of clues that scientists use to make guesses about things they cannot see or test directly.

2. Based upon how it is used in the text, predict what the word means: guesses

3. Consult an "expert" for the actual definition (e.g., a friend, teacher, text resource). Expert: Parent
   Expert's definition: Basing an explanation about something you can't see on what you already know about something.

4. Show your understanding of the word by using it in a sentence of your own: I use indirect evidence to try to figure out what is in my wrapped birthday present.

5. Choose one of the following ways to help you remember the word's meaning: draw a picture of what the word means to you; select and perform a miming action that the word reminds you of; or connect the word with something similar that you've heard — in a story, a news report, or a song. Write down an association or connection you have made: Picture of kid shaking present.

6. Explain why you chose this way to represent what the word means to you: Shaking a present will remind me that indirect evidence involves using all of the senses you can to find the answer to something you can't see.

Notes

Student VOC Strategy

Vocabulary Word: black hole

1. Write the sentence in which it appears in the text:
   A black hole is a region in space that was once occupied by a star.

2. Based upon how it is used in the text, predict what the word means:
   A hole in space.

3. Consult an "expert" for the actual definition (e.g., a friend, teacher, text resource). Expert: Text
   Expert's definition: Small, cold, dark object resulting from cooling of white dwarf.

4. Show your understanding of the word by using it in a sentence of your own: Many white dwarf stars die quietly by becoming black holes.

5. Choose one of the following ways to help you remember the word's meaning: draw a picture of what the word means to you; select and perform a miming action that the word reminds you of; or connect the word with something similar that you've heard — in a story, a news report, or a song. Write down an association or connection you have made: A picture of a white candle dying out and the room becoming black.

6. Explain why you chose this way to represent what the word means to you:
   It shows light (white dwarf) dying down to the blackness (black hole).

Notes

Vocabulary Development

Student VOC Strategy

Vocabulary Word: **mitosis**

1. Write the sentence in which it appears in the text:

   The first stage of cell division is called mitosis.

2. Based upon how it is used in the text, predict what the word means:

   The first part of how the cell divides into 2 cells.

3. Consult an "expert" for the actual definition (e.g., a friend, teacher, text resource). Expert: **Text**

   Expert's definition: **Mitosis is the process by which the nucleus of the cell is divided into nuclei, each with the same number and kind of chromosomes as the parent cell.**

4. Show your understanding of the word by using it in a sentence of your own: **Mitosis produces two identical nuclei.**

5. Choose one of the following ways to help you remember the word's meaning: draw a picture of what the word means to you; select and perform a miming action that the word reminds you of; or connect the word with something similar that you've heard — in a story, a news report, or a song. Write down an association or connection you have made:

6. Explain why you chose this way to represent what the word means to you:

   It shows the nucleus divided, but not the cell.

Preactive
Interactive
Reflective

Notes

S-6. Word Sort

What is it?

Word sorts (Gillett & Temple, 1983) help students recognize the semantic relationships among key concepts printed on 3″ x 5″ cards. This strategy can be used in two different ways. In a "closed sort," the teacher provides categories into which students assign the words. In an "open sort," students group words into categories and create their own labels for each category. Word sorts help students develop a deeper understanding of key concepts. They also can be used to develop the complex reasoning skills of classification and deduction.

How could it be used in science instruction?

This strategy can be used throughout a unit by creating a "word wall," which can be used at various times in various ways. Sorting the words can serve as an *engagement* activity to *evaluate* what students already know about the terms. The cards can be used to *explore* different categories into which the terms may be classified. The cards can be incorporated to help students *explain* their understanding.

How to use it:

1. List terms on 3″ x 5″ cards (one word per card).

2. Allow students, individually or in groups, to sort the words into categories. Depending on the concepts and students' level of understanding, the sorts can be "closed" or "open." Model this process for students by "thinking aloud" as cards are sorted.

3. As students become more proficient at classifying, they should be encouraged to complete "open sorts" and to find more than one way to classify the vocabulary terms. Classifying and then reclassifying helps students *extend* and refine their understanding of the concepts studied.

For further discussion of this strategy, see the *TRCA Teacher's Manual*, p. 89.

Notes

Vocabulary Development

Biome Word Sort

Tundra Biomes	Grassland Biomes	Desert Biomes
Permafrost	Savannas	Sahara
North Pole	Grasses	Cactus
Caribou	Zebras	Aloe plants
Lichens	Giraffes	Camels

Forest Biomes	Water Biomes
Conifers	Marine
Taiga	Phytoplankton
Deciduous	Freshwater
Canopy	Estuary
Tropical	

Vocabulary Development

Notes

Acids and Bases Word Sort

Acids	Bases
HCl	$NaHCO_3$
H_2SO_4	$NaOH$
H_2CO_3	KOH
	NH_4OH

Weather Word Sort

Tools For Measuring Weather	Clouds	Weather Disasters
Thermometer	Cirrus	Hurricanes
Barometer	Cumulus	Tornadoes
Wind gauge	Stratus	Blizzards
Wind vane		Floods

Notes

Informational Text

Preactive
Interactive
Reflective

S-7. Anticipation Guide/ Revised Extended Anticipation Guide

What is it?

Anticipation guides (Herber, 1978) are a set of carefully selected questions that serve as a pre/post inventory for a reading selection. They are designed to activate and assess students' prior knowledge, to focus reading, and to motivate reluctant readers by stimulating their interest in the topic. The revised extended anticipation guides (Duffelmeyer & Baum, 1992) facilitate text comprehension because they require considerable interaction between reader and text. They require students to paraphrase the text when reader-text discrepancies occur and to justify claims of reader-text agreement.

How could it be used in science instruction?

When incorporated during the *engagement* phase, these guides help students focus on and pay attention to critical information. During the *exploration* phase students can search for answers as they read. This strategy is helpful in *evaluating* students' misconceptions.

How to use it:

1. Identify concepts you want students to learn.
2. Create four to six statements that support or challenge students' beliefs and experiences (important points, major concepts, controversial ideas, or misconceptions) about the topic.
3. Prior to reading, students (individually or as a group) react to each statement, formulate a response (under the "me" column), and prepare to defend their opinions.
4. Ask students to *explain* their responses to each statement.
5. Ask students to read the selection to find evidence that supports or disconfirms each statement ("text" column).
6. Lead a discussion about what students learned from their reading.

For further discussion of this strategy, please see the *TRCA Teacher's Manual*, pp. 104–106.

Anticipation Guide
Earthworms

Directions: In the column labeled *Me,* place a check next to any statement with which you agree. After reading the text, compare your opinions about those statements with information contained in the text.

Me	Text	
_____	_____	1. The earthworm has a backbone.
_____	_____	2. Earthworms eat soil to make tunnels.
_____	_____	3. Earthworms breathe through lungs.
_____	_____	4. Farmers like earthworms.

Note. Basic format only from *Teaching Reading in Content Areas,* by H. Herber, 1978, Englewood Cliffs, NJ: Prentice Hall. Copyright 1978 by Prentice Hall.

Anticipation Guide
Matter

Directions: In the column labeled *Me,* place a check next to any statement with which you agree. After reading the text, compare your opinions about those statements with information contained in the text.

Me	Text	
_____	_____	1. Matter is made up of elements.
_____	_____	2. An element is made up of many different atoms.
_____	_____	3. An element is the same thing as a compound.
_____	_____	4. Most compounds are made of molecules.
_____	_____	5. Elements are represented by chemical symbols.
_____	_____	6. Molecules are represented by chemical formulas.

Note. Basic format only from *Teaching Reading in Content Areas,* by H. Herber, 1978, Englewood Cliffs, NJ: Prentice Hall. Copyright 1978 by Prentice Hall.

Notes

Informational Text

Revised Extended Anticipation Guide
Mountains

Part 1:
Directions: Before you read your class assignment, read each statement in Part 1. If you believe that a statement is true, place a check in the *Agree* column. If you believe that a statement is false, place a check in the *Disagree* column. Be ready to explain your choices.

Agree	Disagree	
❑	❑	1. Young mountains have sharper peaks than old mountains.
❑	❑	2. Folded mountains form when continents collide.
❑	❑	3. Fault-block mountains form when magma pushes up the Earth's crust.
❑	❑	4. There are four major mountain belts on the Earth.
❑	❑	5. Narrow valleys are found in mature mountains.

Part 2:
Directions: Now you will read information related to each of the statements in Part 1. If the information supports your choices above, place a check in the *Yes* column in Part 2. Then write what the text says in your own words in column A, under *Why is my choice correct?* If the information does not support your choices, place a check in the *No* column. Then write what the text says in your own words in column B, under *Why is my choice incorrect?*

Support in text for my choice		(A)	(B)
Yes	**No**	Why is my choice correct?	Why is my choice incorrect?
1. ❑	❑	______________________ ______________________	______________________ ______________________
2. ❑	❑	______________________ ______________________	______________________ ______________________
3. ❑	❑	______________________ ______________________	______________________ ______________________
4. ❑	❑	______________________ ______________________	______________________ ______________________
5. ❑	❑	______________________ ______________________	______________________ ______________________

Note. Basic format only from "Open to Suggestion: The Extended Anticipation Guide Revisited," by F. A. Duffelmeyer and D. D. Baum, 1992, *Journal of Reading, 35*(8), pp. 654–56. Copyright 1992 by the International Reading Association.

Notes

Revised Extended Anticipation Guide
AIDS

Part 1:
Directions: Before you read your class assignment, read each statement in Part 1. If you believe that a statement is true, place a check in the *Agree* column. If you believe that a statement is false, place a check in the *Disagree* column. Be ready to explain your choices.

Agree	Disagree		
☑	❑	1.	You can get AIDS by being near someone who has it, just as you can with a cold or the flu.
❑	☑	2.	AIDS kills people by attacking a single organ, like the heart or the lungs.
❑	☑	3.	Because of AIDS, donating blood is no longer safe.
☑	❑	4.	An unborn baby is safe from AIDS as long as the mother doesn't inject drugs.
☑	❑	5.	AIDS can be controlled with extreme rest and care.
☑	❑	6.	Many people with AIDS in this country have died.

Part 2:
Directions: Now you will read information related to each of the statements in Part 1. If the information supports your choices above, place a check in the *Yes* column in Part 2. Then write what the text says in your own words in column A, under *Why is my choice correct?* If the information does not support your choices, place a check in the *No* column. Then write what the text says in your own words in column B, under *Why is my choice incorrect?*

Support in text for my choice

	Yes	No	(A) Why is my choice correct?	(B) Why is my choice incorrect?
1.	❑	☑		AIDS is spread through sex and contaminated blood.
2.	☑	❑	AIDS kills people by attacking their immune system.	
3.	☑	❑	Giving blood is safe because a clean needle is always used.	
4.	❑	☑		A pregnant woman can get AIDS in other ways.
5.	❑	☑		There is no cure for AIDS.
6.	☑	❑	Half of the people with AIDS in this country have died.	

Note. From "Open to Suggestion: The Extended Anticipation Guide Revisited," by F. A. Duffelmeyer and D. D. Baum, 1992, *Journal of Reading, 35*(8), pp. 654–56. Reprinted with permission of Frederick A. Duffelmeyer and the International Reading Association.

Notes

Informational Text

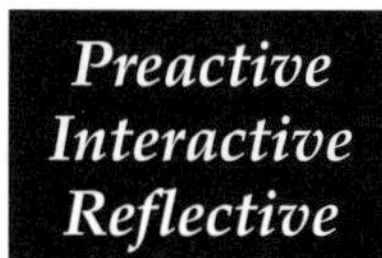

S-8. Directed Reading/ Thinking Activity (DR/TA)

What is it?

The directed reading/thinking activity (Stauffer, 1969) is similar to K-W-L in both concept and versatility. It encourages active reading through activation of prior knowledge, predicting, and checking the accuracy of predictions. It provides students with a system for organizing their thoughts, encourages students to focus on the topic, and gives them a purpose for reading.

How could it be used in science instruction?

This strategy might be used to *engage* students in *exploring* a topic through reading. This strategy might follow an experiment that has provided students with prior knowledge, giving students the opportunity to *explain* what they already know. It might also be used to give students a chance to *elaborate* on what they have learned through their reading. It also provides teachers with the opportunity to *evaluate* students' understanding and check for misconceptions.

How to use it:

1. Instruct students to preview the text selection — noting the title, any subheadings, and graphic aids — and complete the first two sections of the form. This will focus students on the topic. Discussing these sections can expose misconceptions.
2. Ask students to fill out the third section, which requires them to formulate predictions about what they will read and sets the purpose for reading.
3. Instruct students to read the text selection, confirming or rejecting earlier predictions about the subject matter.
4. Following the reading, ask students to complete the last section of the form. This helps to reinforce understanding and to correct misconceptions.

For further discussion of this strategy, see the *TRCA Teacher's Manual*, pp. 107–108.

Directed Reading/Thinking Activity
What I know I know:
What I think I know:
What I think I'll learn:
What I know I learned:

Notes

Informational Text

Directed Reading/Thinking Activity Earth's Surface
What I know I know: hills mountains valleys plains rivers lakes
What I think I know: Volcanoes cause some features. The Earth is always changing.
What I think I'll learn: What are other landforms and features? What caused the landforms?
What I know I learned:

Notes

Directed Reading/Thinking Activity

Flowering Plants and Reproduction

What I know I know:

Flowers have these parts:

sepals	ovary	filament
petals	stigma	pistil
anther		

What I think I know:

Flower structure and functions:
- sepal — base of flower
- petals — attract insects
- anther & filament — male reproductive part
- ovary & stigma — female reproductive part
- pollen grains — male reproductive cell
- ovule — female reproductive cell

What I think I'll learn:

What is the role of fruit?
What is involved in the germination process?
What kinds of plants reproduce without seeds?
Why are some people allergic to pollen?
What makes a plant grow?
What is the role of plant hormones?
What is the difference between annual, biennial, and perennial?

What I know I learned:

Notes

Directed Reading/Thinking Activity Metals & Nonmetals
What I know I know: Metals conduct electricity. Metals are useful.
What I think I know: Metals are hard and shiny and can bend. Nonmetals form compounds more easily.
What I think I'll learn: Where they are on the Periodic Table.
What I know I learned:

Informational Text

Preactive
Interactive
Reflective

S-9. Graphic Organizer

What is it?

Graphic organizers include things like webs, maps, and diagrams. They provide a visual representation of key concepts and related terms, help students see relationships among ideas, and show how ideas link together. They are effective tools for thinking, note taking, and learning. They help students represent abstract ideas in more concrete forms, depict relationships among facts and concepts, organize ideas, and store or recall information.

Graphic organizers can be used to depict various aspects or elements of a concept and the relationships among them. They can also be constructed around a common organizational pattern such as those described on page 21 of this supplement.

How could it be used in science instruction?

This strategy can be incorporated throughout a lesson or unit. It can be used to *engage* students by having them share what they know about a topic. Graphic organizers can help students to *explore* connections, *explain* relationships, and *elaborate* on what they have learned. Throughout the lesson or unit, a teacher can *evaluate* students' understanding and check for misconceptions.

How to use it:

1. Explain the purpose and benefits of using graphic organizers.
2. Introduce a specific form of graphic organizer.
3. Model how to use the selected organizer.
4. Provide multiple opportunities for students to practice using graphic organizers.
5. Encourage students to construct their own organizers.

For further discussion of this strategy, see the *TRCA Teacher's Manual*, pp. 109–111, 134, and 135.

Notes

Notes

Informational Text

Concept Definition Web

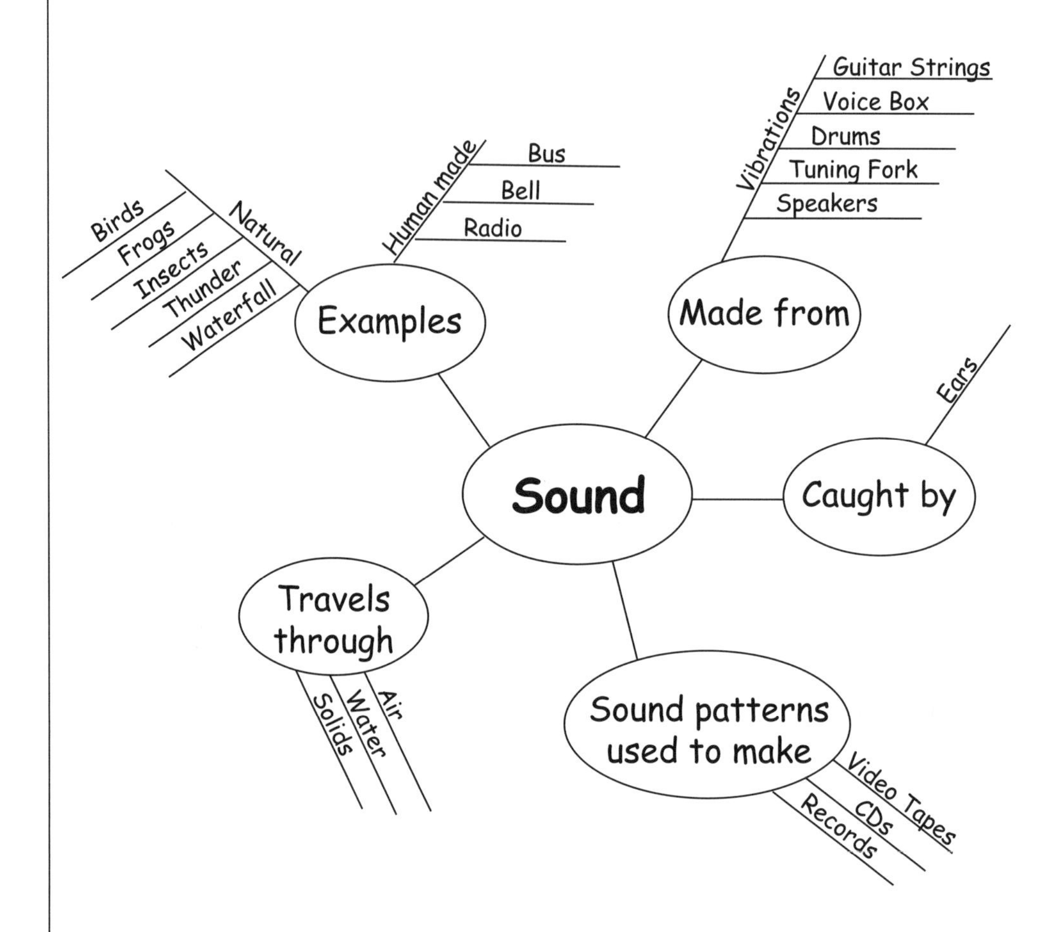

Notes

Concept Definition Web

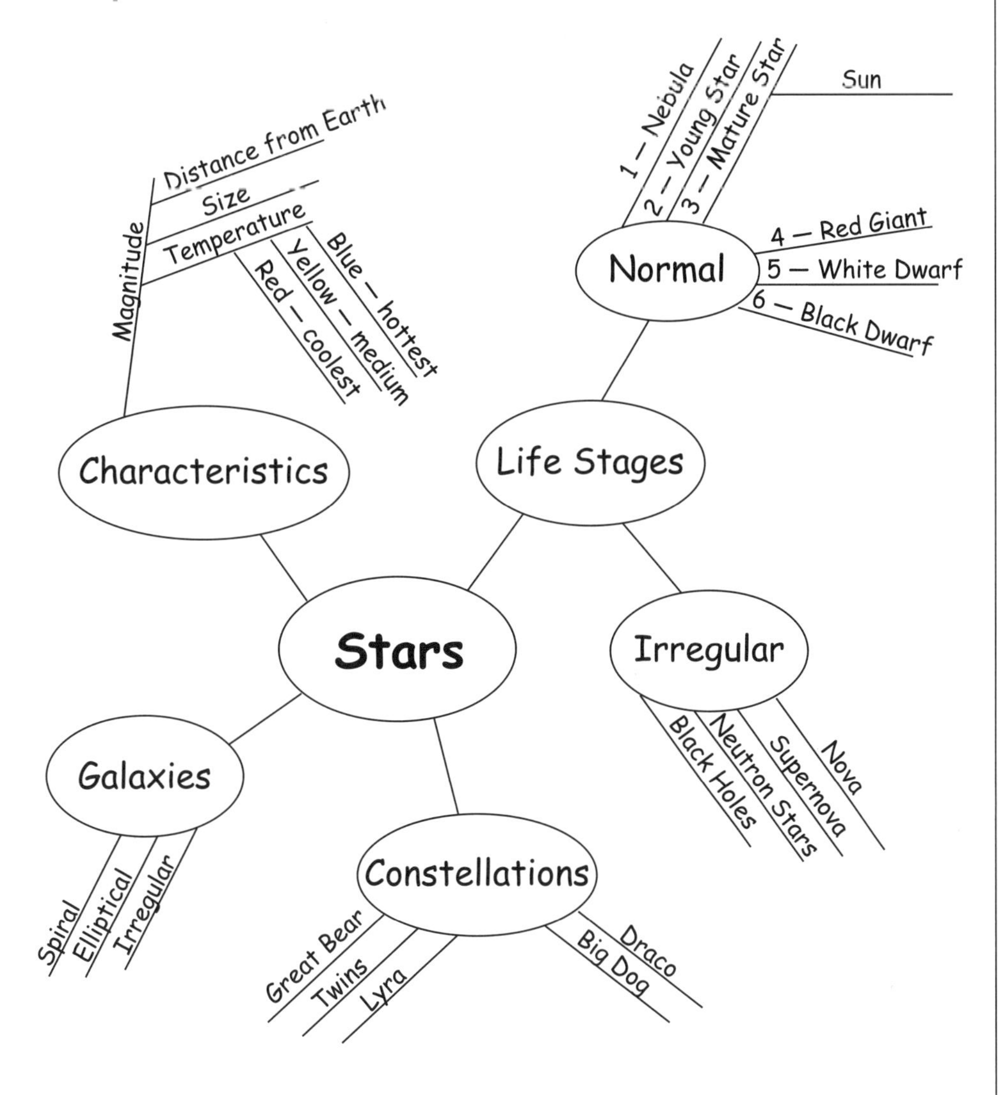

Notes

Informational Text

Concept Definition Web

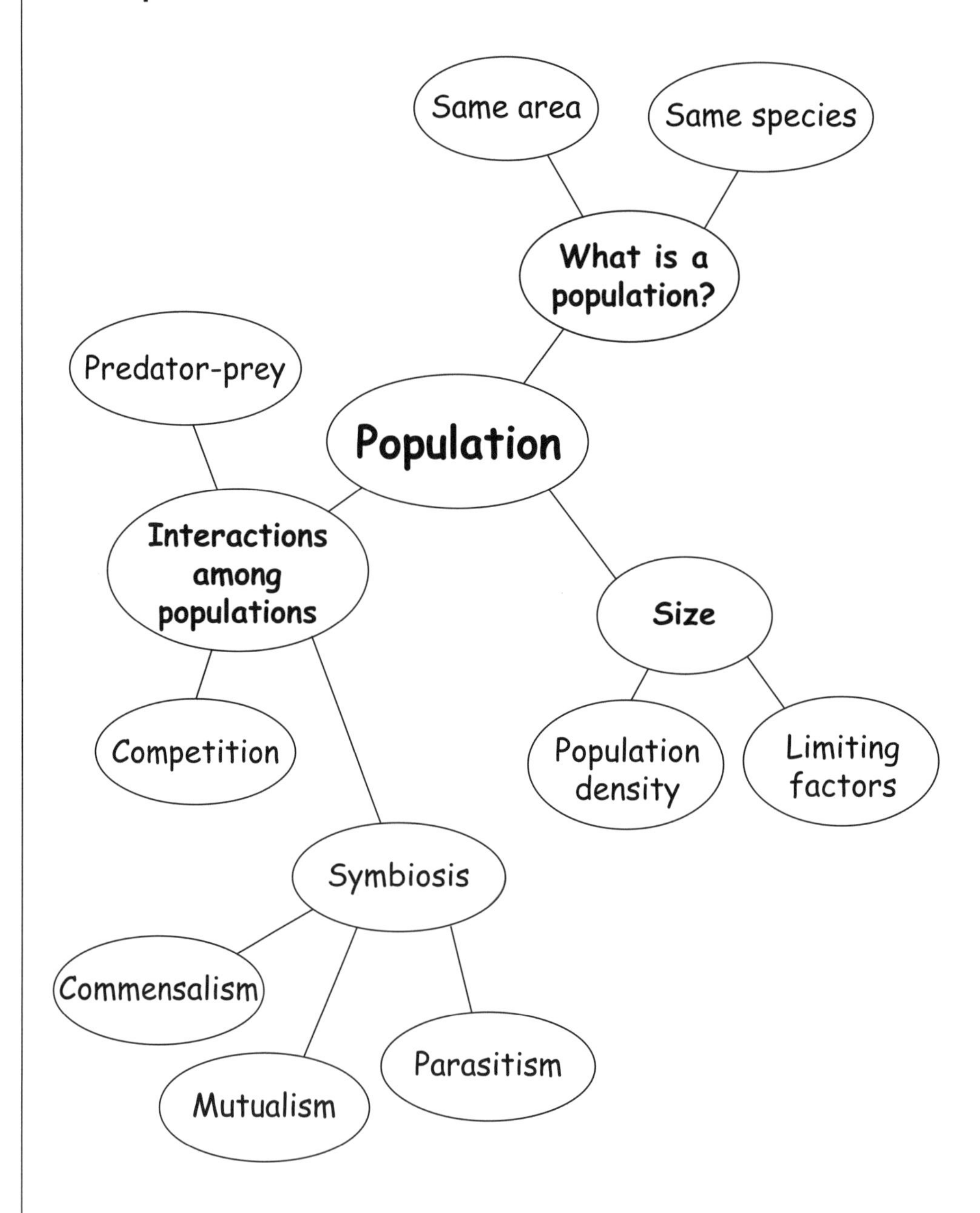

Informational Text

Description Web

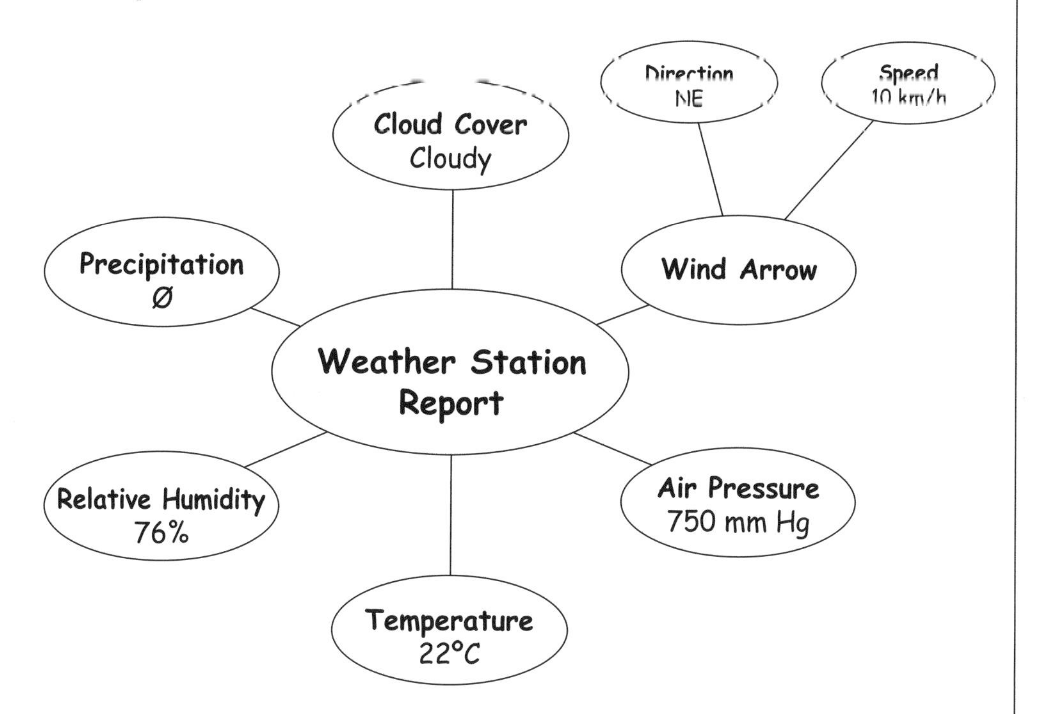

Compare/Contrast Venn Diagram

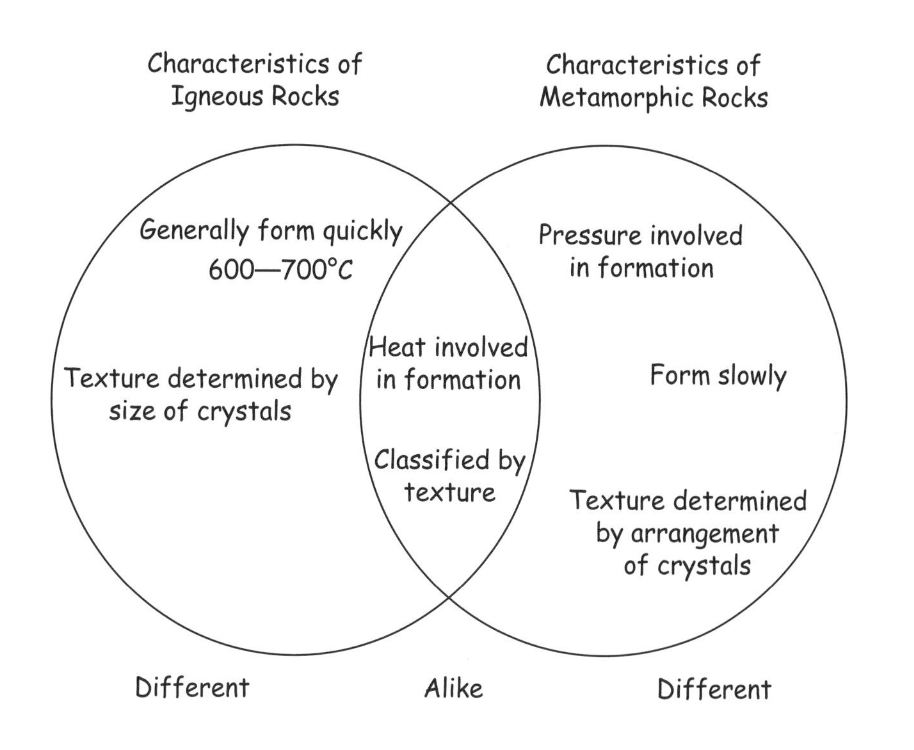

Notes

Notes

Informational Text

Generalization/Principle Diagram

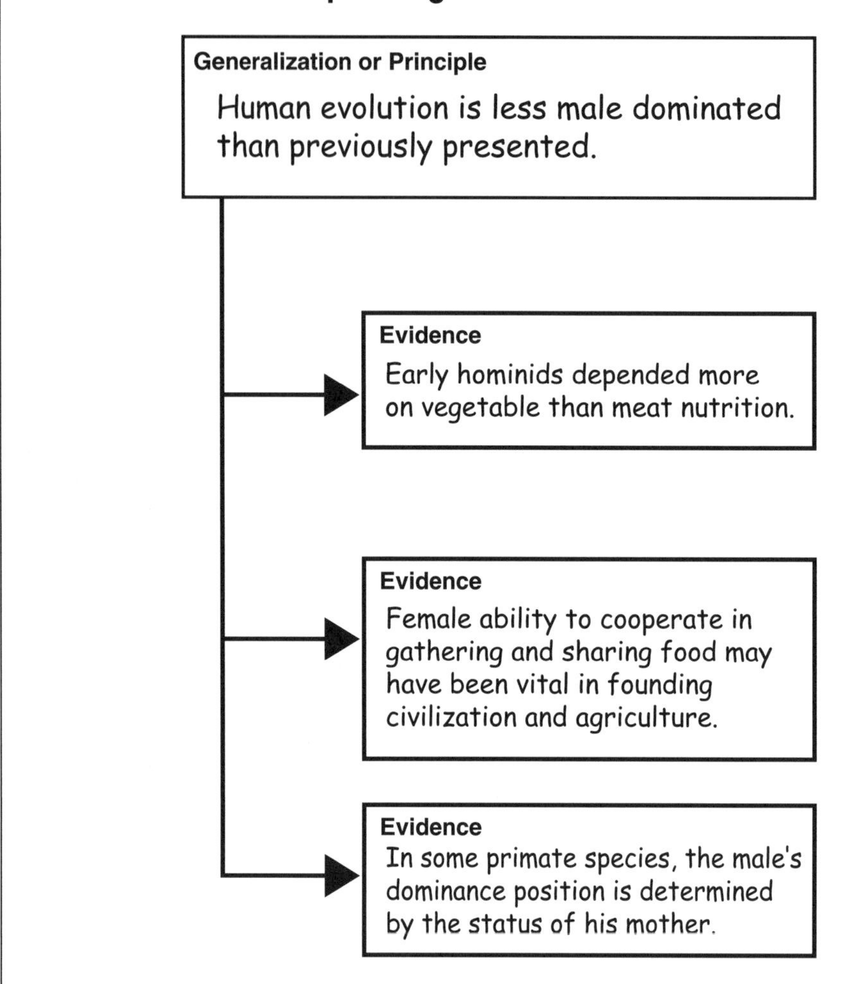

Process/Cause-Effect Diagram

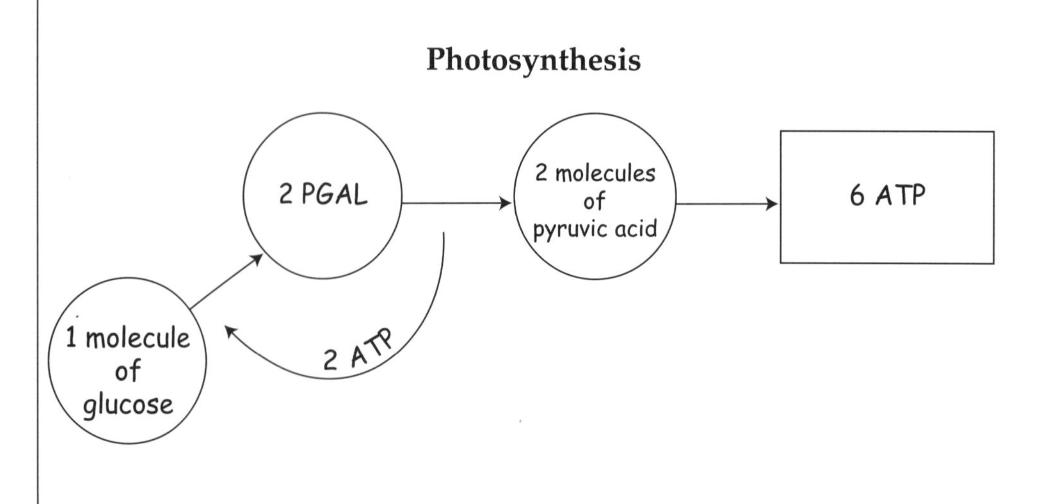

Notes

S-10. Group Summarizing

What is it?

Class summaries help learners review and remember information. Summarizing information requires readers to distinguish between key concepts and subordinate ideas. It also requires the ability to condense information (Brown, Day, & Jones, 1983). Summarizing is a sophisticated skill; therefore, modeling is critical.

How could it be used in science instruction?

This strategy is helpful when you want students to *explain* what they have learned through a summary. This strategy models for students how to write a report about what they have learned.

How to use it:

1. Instruct students to survey the text passage to identify major topics to focus on while reading.
2. Next, divide the chalkboard or chart paper into parts and label the sections based on major topics. These sections provide students with a purpose for reading.
3. After students have read the text, ask for volunteers to provide information for each of the categories. Record the information in sentence form on chart paper. Class discussion is a key part of the process. Students need to decide what information is critical and how to state it clearly.
4. The critical information is then transferred to the appropriate labeled sections of the chart.
5. To help students learn to identify major topics, modify this strategy by recording student information first. Ask students to identify major topics and then organize the information into identified topics.

For further discussion of this strategy, see the *TRCA Teacher's Manual*, pp. 112–113.

Notes

Informational Text

Sample Organizational Format for Group Summarizing Activity

Armadillos	
Description Nine-banded armadillos are about two feet long and weigh about fifteen pounds. They have strong claws for digging and a shell of hard, bony plates for protection.	**Food** Armadillos eat insects, earthworms, spiders, and landsnails by licking them up.
Home Armadillos live in a tunnel hole filled with leaves to keep them warm.	**Interesting Facts** Armadillos protect themselves by digging a hole or curling into a ball. They have four babies at a time that are all males or all females.

Note. From "Content Reading Instruction in the Primary Grades: Perceptions and Strategies," by M. W. Olson and T. C. Gee, 1991, *The Reading Teacher, 45*(4), pp. 298–307. Reprinted with permission of Mary W. Olson and the International Reading Association.

Notes

Giraffes	
Description Giraffes have skin patterns and colors that make them hard to see. Giraffes have very long necks (six feet or longer). They have very long tongues that help them gather leaves and twigs from treetops.	**Food** Giraffes eat leaves and flowers from the acacia tree.
Home All wild giraffes live in herds in the grasslands of Africa.	**Interesting Facts** Giraffes are the tallest animals in the world. They have one baby at a time. They can run about 30 miles per hour.

Note. Basic format only from "Content Reading Instruction in the Primary Grades: Perceptions and Strategies," by M. W. Olson and T. C. Gee, 1991, *The Reading Teacher, 45*(4), pp. 298–307. Copyright 1991 by the International Reading Association.

Soil	
Description Soil is a mixture mainly containing weathered rock, minerals, and humus. Air and water fill spaces between soil particles.	**Formation** When bedrock is weathered, it breaks down into smaller particles. These particles are further weathered into soil.
Living Things Many organisms live on the soil and in it. Some living things, like moss, lichens, bacteria, and fungi, form into soil through decomposition. Humus is the decayed remains of dead plants and animals.	**Importance** Soil provides water, nutrients, and support to plants. Soil nutrients may be used faster by plants than they can be replaced.

Note. Basic format only from "Content Reading Instruction in the Primary Grades: Perceptions and Strategies," by M. W. Olson and T. C. Gee, 1991, *The Reading Teacher, 45*(4), pp. 298–307. Copyright 1991 by the International Reading Association.

Notes

Informational Text

Electricity	
Description Electricity is one kind of energy.	**Kinds of Electricity** There are two kinds of electricity, static and current. Static electricity is an electric charge that does not move. Current electricity is the movement of electrons.
Electric Circuits There are two kinds of electric circuits. A series circuit is one in which current can follow only one path. A parallel circuit is one in which current can follow more than one path.	**Producing Electricity** A generator is a machine that changes mechanical energy into electrical energy. A dry cell uses a chemical paste, carbon rod, and zinc to produce a flow of electrons. A wet cell uses acid and water, which reacts with metal plates, to produce a flow of electrons.
Using Electricity Electricity is an important source of light and heat. Electrical energy can be changed to mechanical energy. Fuses and circuit breakers are safety devices designed to help use electricity safely.	**Measuring Electricity** The amount of electricity used is measured in kilowatt-hours.

Note. Basic format only from "Content Reading Instruction in the Primary Grades: Perceptions and Strategies," by M. W. Olson and T. C. Gee, 1991, *The Reading Teacher, 45*(4), pp. 298–307. Copyright 1991 by the International Reading Association.

Informational Text

Preactive
Reflective

Notes

S-11. What I Know; Want to Learn; Learned (K-W-L)

What is it?

Another strategy that helps students predict and connect new information with prior knowledge is K-W-L (Ogle, 1986, 1989). K-W-L can be used to brainstorm prior knowledge, to preview vocabulary and/or concepts, and to help students recall what they have read.

How could it be used in science instruction?

This strategy could be used to *engage* students to *explore* a topic through reading. It might follow an experiment that has provided students with prior knowledge, giving students the opportunity to *explain* what they already know. It gives them a chance to *elaborate* on what they have learned through their reading. It also provides teachers with the opportunity to *evaluate* students' understanding and check for misconceptions.

How to use it:

1. Provide a K-W-L chart to students.
2. Instruct students to fill out the first two sections of the chart. Student misconceptions generally show up in the "What I Know" column.
3. Students read the text selection purposefully to discover answers for the questions they have posed.
4. Ask students to identify what they have learned. Then ask them to record answers to their questions as well as any other important information they have learned. Sometimes students find out that their prior knowledge was inaccurate.

For further discussion of this strategy, including variations, see the *TRCA Teacher's Manual*, pp. 116–118.

Notes

Informational Text

K-W-L Worksheet

K What I know	W What I want to find out	L What I learned

Note. From "Content Reading Instruction in the Primary Grades: Perceptions and Strategies," by M. W. Olson and T. C. Gee, 1991, *The Reading Teacher, 45*(4), pp. 298–307. Reprinted with permission of Mary W. Olson and the International Reading Association.

K-W-L Worksheet: Water

K What I know	W What I want to find out	L What I learned
Water appears on Earth, as a solid, liquid, and a gas. Water is important for life. There is a water cycle.	How do plants conserve water? Why do some objects sink and other objects float? Can we avoid polluting our water supply?	

Note. Basic format only from "Content Reading Instruction in the Primary Grades: Perceptions and Strategies," by M. W. Olson and T. C. Gee, 1991, *The Reading Teacher, 45*(4), pp. 298–307. Copyright 1991 by the International Reading Association.

K-W-L Worksheet: Cycles in Time

K What I know	W What I want to find out	L What I learned
Some trees change colors. Some animals migrate. Some animals are active at night. Some animals hibernate.	What controls the rhythms of life? • Daily • Lunar • Annual	

Note. Basic format only from "Content Reading Instruction in the Primary Grades: Perceptions and Strategies," by M. W. Olson and T. C. Gee, 1991, *The Reading Teacher, 45*(4), pp. 298–307. Copyright 1991 by the International Reading Association.

K-W-L Worksheet: Phases of Matter

K What I know	W What I want to find out	L What I learned
There are three phases of matter. • Solid • Liquid • Gas	Why does temperature make a difference? How are atoms arranged? How can phases change in both directions?	

Note. Basic format only from "Content Reading Instruction in the Primary Grades: Perceptions and Strategies," by M. W. Olson and T. C. Gee, 1991, *The Reading Teacher, 45*(4), pp. 298–307. Copyright 1991 by the International Reading Association.

Notes

Informational Text

Interactive

S-12. Pairs Read

What is it?

Pairs read is a strategy that requires collaborative learning as students read and digest text. Students help each other increase their knowledge and understanding of the text by reading the text aloud to each other. While one student reads aloud, the other student listens and then summarizes the main ideas.

How could it be used in science instruction?

This strategy provides students with opportunities to *explore* information from a variety of sources, such as articles or trade books, on the same topic. Students read information in pairs and then share what they have learned about the topic with the rest of the class.

How to use it:

1. Select a passage for students to read.
2. Arrange students into pairs with one being the coach and the other being the reader.
3. Ask the reader to read the first paragraph aloud to the coach.
4. Then ask the coach to summarize the main idea and supporting details. The coach can ask the reader questions to help clarify the reading.
5. Instruct students to reverse roles and ask the new reader to read the next paragraph.
6. Ask the new coach to summarize what was read.
7. Instruct students to continue alternating roles until they have completed the passage.
8. Once the entire passage is read, ask students to cooperatively summarize the main idea and discuss the supporting details.

For further discussion of this strategy, including variations, see the *TRCA Teacher's Manual*, pp. 119–120.

Informational Text

S-13. Predict; Locate; Add; Note (PLAN)

Preactive
Interactive
Reflective

Notes

What is it?

PLAN is a study-reading strategy for informational text that helps students read strategically (Caverly, Mandeville, & Nicholson, 1995). PLAN is an acronym for four distinct steps that students are taught to use before, during, and after reading. The first step is to *predict* the content and text structure; students create a probable map or diagram based on chapter title, subtitles, highlighted words, and information from graphics. The second step is to *locate* known and unknown information on the map by placing checkmarks (✔) next to familiar concepts and question marks (**?**) next to unfamiliar concepts; this causes students to activate and assess their prior knowledge about the topic. The third step, *add*, is applied as students read; they add words or short phrases to their map to explain concepts marked with question marks or confirm and extend known concepts marked with checks. *Note* is the fourth step; after reading, students note their new understanding by using this new knowledge to fulfill a task (e.g., reproducing the map from memory, writing in their learning log, discussing what they have learned, or writing a summary). This reinforces their learning and ensures that they have fulfilled their purposes for reading.

How could it be used in science instruction?

Much of what is written in science follows one of the five patterns discussed earlier in this manual: compare/contrast, concept definition, description, generalization/principle, or process/cause-effect. However, when text does not appear to be organized according to one of these patterns, PLAN provides students with another way to *explore* the relationships among the ideas in the text and to create a visual they can use to take notes while reading. Using graphic organizers also helps students to see connections as they construct their understanding of science concepts. PLAN encourages students to self-*evaluate* what they know about a topic. It also provides an opportunity for students to *explain* and *elaborate* on what they know or have learned through their reading.

How to use it:

1. Model the four PLAN steps (Predict; Locate; Add; and Note) for students.
2. Give students opportunities to practice using the PLAN strategy with various organizational patterns.

Step 1: Predict

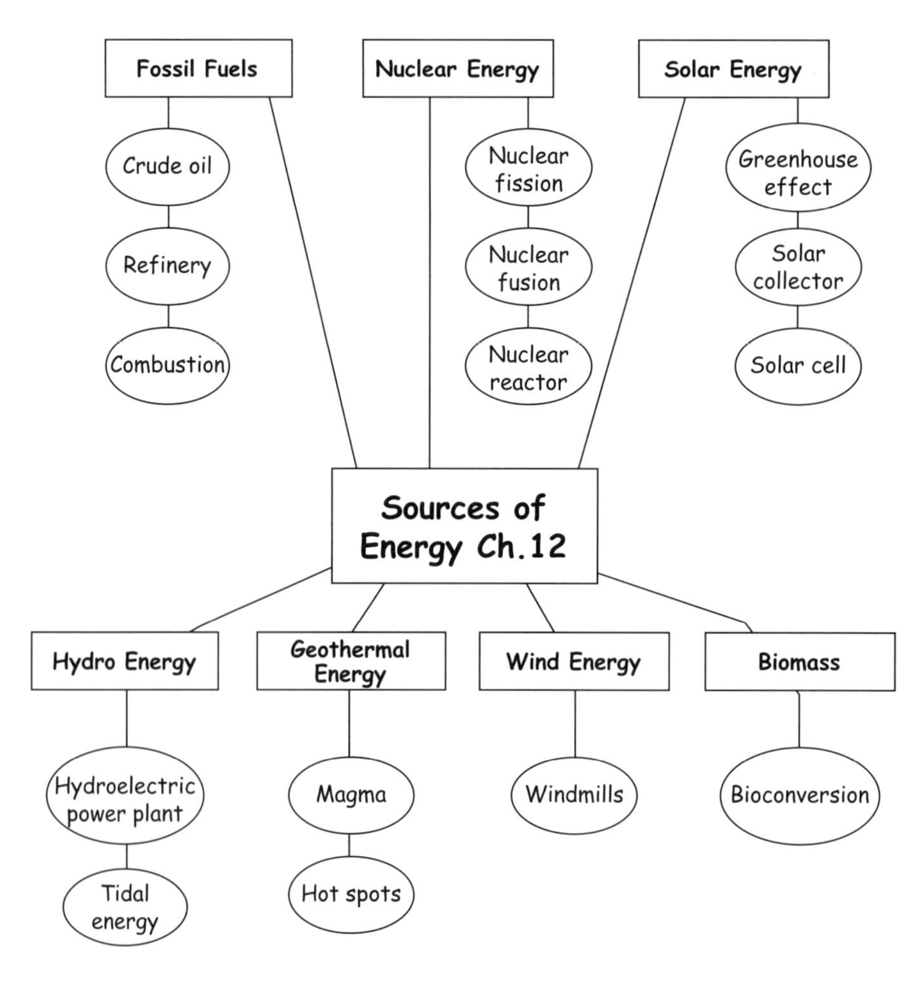

Notes

Step 2: Locate

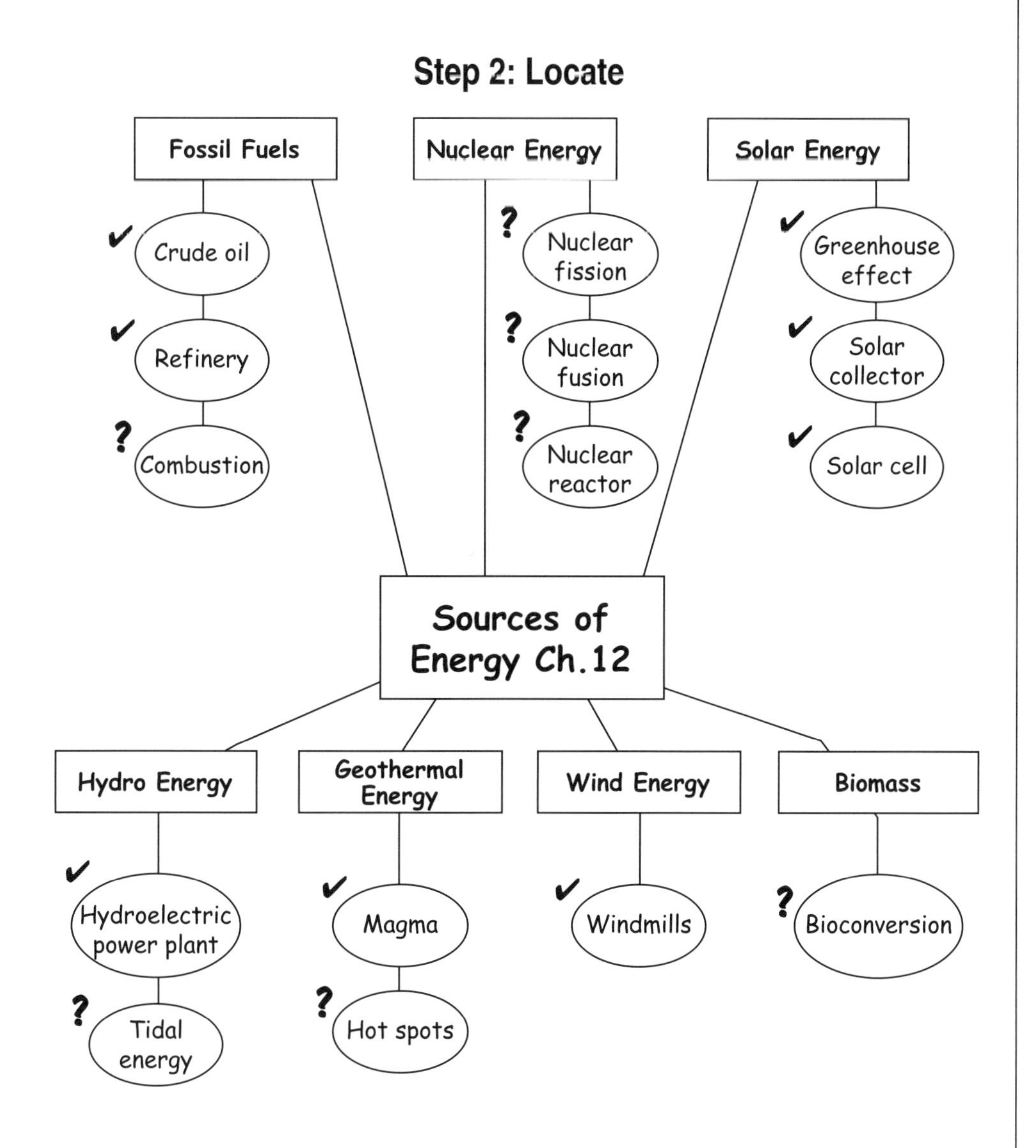

Notes

Informational Text

Step 3: Add

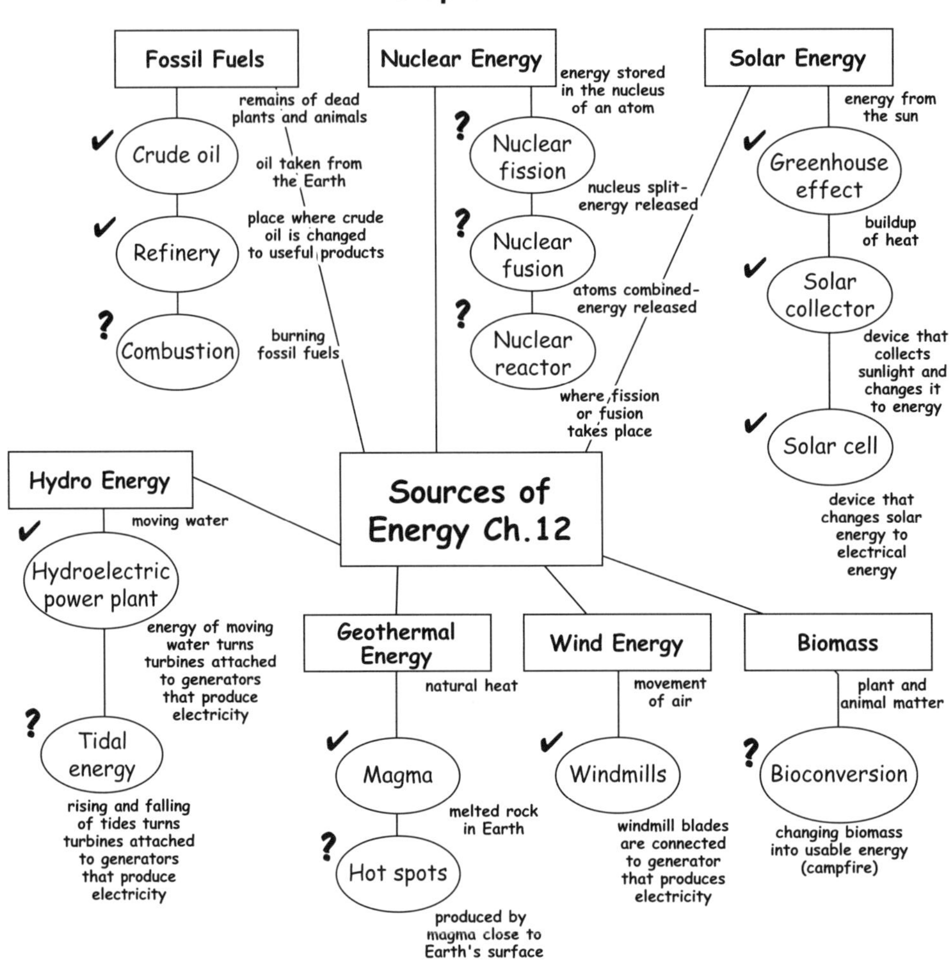

Note. Basic format only from "PLAN: A Study Reading Strategy for Informational Text," by D. C. Caverly, T. F. Mandeville, and S. A. Nicholson, 1995, *Journal of Adolescent and Adult Literacy, 39*(3), pp. 190–199. Copyright 1995 by the International Reading Association.

Preactive
Reflective

Notes

S-14. Problematic Situation

What is it?

Problematic situation is a strategy that activates what students already know about a topic, motivates students to want to read the text, and helps them to focus on the main ideas presented in the text as they read. Developed by Vacca and Vacca (1993), it can be used with any text material dealing with a problem/solution relationship.

How could it be used in science instruction?

This strategy can be used to *engage* students to *explore* ideas through reading. It can also be used to *evaluate* students' understanding of content. This strategy is an effective way to address personal and social issues in science.

How to use it:

1. Design a problematic situation similar to one presented in a selected text passage. Provide enough relevant information about the situation so students will be able to focus their attention on key ideas in the passage. Be sure to clearly define the context of the problem.

2. Pose the problem to students. Let cooperative groups generate possible results or solutions, recording their responses. When they have listed their solutions, let them discuss why each one is a good solution or why it would succeed.

3. Ask students to "test" their solutions when they read the assigned text material. Each group should refine or modify their solutions as they gain new information from their reading.

4. As a final activity, discuss with the class whether some of the students' solutions might be better than those presented by the author.

For further discussion of this strategy, see the *TRCA Teacher's Manual*, pp. 122–123.

Notes

Informational Text

Problematic Situation Examples

Protecting Wildlife

Our planet supports a wide variety of wildlife. Some species are in great danger. Humans are polluting and destroying many natural places in the world and pushing wildlife into the remotest areas. Some of the most rare animals are still being hunted for their fur and tusks. As a result, creatures such as great whales, rhinoceroses, elephants, and cheetahs could face extinction. What steps would you take in this situation?

Switches

An electrician wants two different lights to be controlled by two different switches. One switch turns only one light on and off. The other switch turns both lights on and off. How can this be accomplished most efficiently?

Global Warming

Some gases produced on Earth are helpful to the environment. Carbon dioxide exists naturally in the atmosphere; it covers the Earth and traps heat from the sun. Without carbon dioxide in the air, the temperature on the Earth would be too cold for living things. However, because people are burning vast amounts of fossil fuels, huge amounts of carbon dioxide are being released into the air. By 2060, some scientists predict that average temperatures will rise 1.5 to 4.5 degrees Celsius. This could mean droughts, severe storms, and flooding. What steps would you take to prevent this situation?

Interactive
Reflective

Notes

S-15. Proposition/Support Outline

What is it?

Proposition/support outlines (Buehl, 1995) help students learn to be critical readers who can recognize different viewpoints, theories, hypotheses, and debatable assertions made by authors. In addition, proposition/support outlines offer students a framework for analyzing the different types of evidence an author presents to support a proposition.

How could it be used in science instruction?

This strategy provides students with a tool to *explore* important science issues by recognizing and categorizing different types of evidence. It can help students see how to use scientific information to make informed decisions.

How to use it:

1. Initiate a discussion of the difference between facts and opinions by brainstorming with students a definition of each and then generating a list of examples for each.
2. Introduce the term "proposition" — a statement that can be argued as true. In science, this may mean a theory, generalization, or a hypothesis. Provide students with several possible propositions; for example, we are using too much energy, loss of our rainforests will lead to environmental disaster, or acid rain is destroying our forests and lakes. Divide students into cooperative groups and assign each group the task of generating as many arguments as possible that might be used to support one of these propositions.
3. Explain that support for a proposition can be categorized as facts, statistics, examples, expert authority, or logic.
4. Assign a text passage that follows a proposition/support frame of writing, and ask students to complete the proposition/support outline as they analyze the author's arguments.
5. Analyze with students the type of support presented.

Notes

Informational Text

This strategy provides students with a framework for examining relevant information and arguments that could be incorporated with other strategies within this supplement such as creative debate (pp. 109–110), discussion web (pp. 111–113), and scored discussion (pp. 124–125).

For further discussion of this strategy, please see the *TRCA Teacher's Manual*, pp. 124–127.

Proposition/Support Outline

Topic:

Proposition:

Support:

1. Facts

2. Statistics

3. Examples

4. Expert Authority

5. Logic and Reasoning

Note. From *Classroom Strategies for Interactive Learning, Second Edition,* by D. Buehl, 2001, Newark, DE: International Reading Association.

Notes

Proposition/Support Outline

Topic:	Rain Forests
Proposition:	The loss of our rain forests will lead to an environmental disaster.

Support:

1. Facts
- Rain forests use up carbon dioxide.
- There is increased carbon dioxide in the earth's atmosphere.
- The rain forests contain many endangered plant and animal species.
- Deforestation leads to widespread soil erosion in many areas.
- The burning of fossil fuels puts carbon dioxide into the environment.

2. Statistics
- The 1980s were the "hottest" decade in the last 100 years.
- One acre of tropical forest disappears every second.
- 4 million acres (larger than the state of Connecticut) disappear every year.
- 50 to 100 species are destroyed with each acre of rain forest cleared.
- If present trends continue, half of the rain forests of Honduras and Nicaragua will disappear by the year 2000.

3. Examples
- India has almost no remaining rain forest.
- Current plans target elimintating much of the Congo's rain forest.
- Run-off from deforestation in Indonesia threatens their coral reefs and diminishes the fish population.
- Cutting of rain forests in Bangladesh and the Phillipines has led to killer floods.

4. Expert Authority
- Computers predict doubling of carbon dioxide in the next century, raising temperatures 3 to 9 degrees.
- National Center for Atmospheric Research believes increased carbon dioxide will lead to Greenhouse Effect and global warming.
- Environmentalist expert Al Gore calls Greenhouse Effect our most serious threat ever.

5. Logic and Reasoning
- Warmer temperatures will harm crops and increase energy costs.
- More people will starve because of less food and increased population growth.
- The polar glaciers will melt and raise the sea level, flooding coastlines.
- Many species useful to humans will disappear.
- More sections of the world will become uninhabitable deserts due to soil loss from erosion, overgrazing, and overcultivation.

Note: From *Classroom Strategies for Interactive Learning, Second Edition,* by Doug Buehl, 1995, Schofield, WI: Wisconsin State Reading Association.

Notes

Informational Text

Proposition/Support Outline

Topic: Genetic Engineering

Proposition: Biologists can engineer a set of genetic changes directly into an organism's DNA.

Support:

1. **Facts**
   - Genes can be cut at specific DNA sequences by using restriction enzymes.
   - The gene must be combined with a piece of DNA from the recipient organism.
   - The combined DNA must be inserted into the new organism.

2. **Statistics**
   - In the last 2 decades, molecular biologists have developed a powerful new set of techniques that affect DNA directly.
   - 75 different restriction enzymes are known.
   - More than 15 years ago, human growth hormone was harvested from cadavers.

3. **Examples**
   - Transgenic bacteria produce human growth hormone and human insulin.
   - Transgenic plants — high-protein alfalfa, nonspoiling tomato.
   - Transgenic animals — faster-growing carp.

4. **Expert Authority**
   - Michael Han (Consumer Policy Institute) says the federal regulatory process is inadequate (about genetic engineering).
   - Jeffery Burkhardt (U. of Fla; agricultural ethics) says, "We need to spend some time talking about our ethical repsonsibilities as well as keeping markets open."

5. **Logic and Reasoning**
   - Human DNA can be analyzed to detect genetic diseases.
   - The technology exists to determine the sequence of the entire human genome.
   - There are many ethical considerations that must be taken into consideration before new genetic engineering techniques are applied to humans.

Note. Basic format only from *Classroom Strategies for Interactive Learning, Second Edition,* by D. Buehl, 2001, Newark, DE: International Reading Association. Copyright 2001 by the International Reading Association.

Preactive
Interactive
Reflective

Notes

S-16. Reciprocal Teaching

What is it?

Reciprocal teaching (Palincsar & Brown, 1985) is a strategy in which students learn the skills of summarizing, questioning, clarifying, and predicting well enough to perform as an instructor of content. When students become adept at these four skills, they not only instruct one another but also learn *metacomprehension* (strategic processing) skills they can use while reading independently.

How could it be used in science instruction?

Reciprocal teaching provides students with opportunities to *explore* science text and to *explain* to other students how to effectively read and comprehend science material.

How to use it:

1. Explain to students the concept of reciprocal teaching — that we learn best by teaching others.
2. Instruct students in the four skills that they will use to improve their own reading comprehension as well as their classmates' (summarizing, questioning, clarifying, and predicting).
3. While reading a text selection, model for students how to summarize, generate questions, clarify confusing text, and predict. Give students time to practice these skills.
4. Begin to shift some of the responsibility for directing class discussions to the students. Allow them to summarize, generate questions, clarify confusing text, and predict for the class.
5. As students become more proficient, let them take turns leading reading discussions for small groups.

For further discussion of this strategy, see the *TRCA Teacher's Manual*, pp. 128–129.

Notes

Informational Text

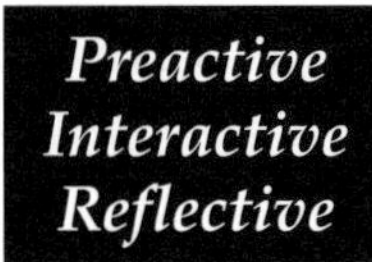

S-17. Survey, Question, Read, Recite, Review (SQ3R)

What is it?

SQ3R (Robinson, 1961) is a versatile study strategy because it engages students during each phase of the reading process. Students preview the text material to develop predictions and to set a purpose for reading by generating questions about the topic; they read actively, searching for answers to those questions; they monitor their comprehension as they summarize; and they evaluate their comprehension through review activities.

How could it be used in science instruction?

This strategy provides students with a structured way to preview and read as they *explore* text material.

How to use it:

1. Provide students with SQ3R instructions on pages 130 and 131 of the *TRCA Teacher's Manual.*
2. Model the strategy for them.
3. Give students time to practice.

For further discussion of this strategy, see the *TRCA Teacher's Manual*, pp. 130–131.

Notes

S-18. Think-Aloud

What is it?

Think-alouds (Davey, 1983) help students understand the kind of thinking required by a specific task. The teacher models a thinking process by verbalizing thoughts while reading, processing information, or performing some learning task. Students see how the teacher attempts to construct meaning for unfamiliar vocabulary, engages in dialogue with the author, or recognizes non-comprehension and selects a strategy to help with comprehension. Struggling readers especially benefit from observing what skilled readers think about while they read.

How could it be used in science instruction?

Think-alouds provide opportunities for teachers to model how to *explore* science text. This might include previewing a chapter by looking at titles, subtitles, graphic organizers, and pictures to get an overall view of what the chapter is going to be about. It might include making predictions, creating mental pictures, connecting information to prior knowledge, creating analogies, and verbalizing obstacles as well as strategies to overcome obstacles while reading science material.

How to use it:

1. Explain that reading is an active process that involves thinking and sense-making.
2. Select a passage to read aloud that students might find difficult.
3. While students read this passage silently, read it aloud. As you read, verbalize your thoughts, your questions, and the processes you use to solve comprehension problems.

For further discussion of this strategy, see the *TRCA Teacher's Manual*, pp. 139–141.

Informational Text

Following launch aboard a Boeing Delta II rocket, the Genesis spacecraft will travel to a point in the solar system called L1. It's a libration point, and these are special points, located throughout the universe, that can be used for low fuel trajectories (paths that require less-than-normal fuel). These points are called libration points. Librate is a verb that means to swing slightly in opposite directions, like the needle on a bathroom scale when it is coming to a rest. An object librates because it is being affected by two opposing forces. Libration points in space are places between two orbiting objects where the gravitational force exerted by the objects on each other is balanced. The Genesis spacecraft will remain at one of these libration points and collect solar wind for two years. As the Earth journeys around the sun, the location of the sun-Earth libration points stays constant with respect to those two solar system objects, but moves from the perspective of a fictional observer hovering over the Milky Way galaxy in a spaceship. An object, natural or man-made, which is at one of the libration points will remain stationary, as observed from Earth, unless acted on by some additional force. A satellite can also be made to orbit one of these points. After its nearly three-year orbit, the spacecraft will return to the Earth.

L1? Did I get that right? Better reread to make sense.

Libration point. I wonder what that is.

Trajectories. Since I can't break it down into smaller words, I'd better look it up.

Okay, now I get it. It's like driving downhill; it takes less fuel.

Yeah, I've seen that.

Like playing with magnets.

Solar wind. What's that? I'll read ahead to see if that term is explained. If it isn't, I'll have to look it up or ask my teacher what it means.

Huh? I didn't get that. I better reread it.

I'm getting a picture in my head of an activity I've seen. A paperclip was attached to a string and suspended in air because of the force of a magnet.

Wow, three years; that's a long time!

Note. Text from "Cool Stuff About Genesis," by McREL, 2001. Retrieved from http://www.genesismission.org/product/genesis_kids/aboutgenesis/aboutgenesis/html

Notes

S-19. Creative Debate

What is it?

The creative debate strategy promotes discussion, original thinking, and thinking from different perspectives. Students debate a topic from a character's point of view.

How could it be used in science instruction?

This strategy gives students the opportunity to *engage* intelligently in public discourse and debate, *exploring* past and present matters of scientific concern. It encourages students to look at both sides of an issue, weigh the facts, and make an informed decision. These are necessary skills for scientifically literate citizenship.

How to use it:

1. Assign students a reading passage with a relevant debate topic.
2. Establish debate criteria.
3. Two-thirds of the class will debate while the remaining third of the class observes.
4. Debaters should be in two rows, facing each other. One row of students should support the issue; the other row should oppose the issue. Students do not have to agree with the positions they are representing.
5. Each student selects a character to portray and takes on the mannerisms and voice of the character during the debate.
6. Students debate from their character's point of view for ten minutes while the observers collect data.
7. Provide time for students to discuss the activity. Encourage the observers to share the data they collect. Reflective questions might include, "How difficult was it to share information from a different perspective? What did you learn? What might you do differently next time?"

For further discussion of this strategy, see the *TRCA Teacher's Manual*, pp. 158–159.

Notes

Reflection Strategies

Examples of Debate Topics

- Everybody can do science.
- Potential research subjects should be told about both the risks and benefits of the research projects.
- New technology can change cultural values and social behavior.
- Any belief about the world is as valid as any other.
- Animals should not be used as research subjects.
- The international community should adopt and enforce laws to prevent further global warming.
- Companies should be allowed to drill for oil in protected wilderness areas.
- Cloning of humans should be allowed.
- Funding for future space programs should be reduced.
- Unwanted, frozen, human embryos should be used for genetics research.
- Genetically engineered food crops are safe for human consumption.

Notes

S-20. Discussion Web

What is it?

The discussion web gives all students, not just those who are verbally talented, an opportunity to assume responsibility and share their own ideas in discussion. Tailored after McTighe and Lyman's (1988) think-pair-share discussion cycle, the discussion web encourages independent thinking before sharing ideas with others. This private "think time" promotes total class involvement and honors the wait time necessary for developing insightful thoughts to share.

How could it be used in science instruction?

This strategy *engages* students intelligently in public discourse and debate, *exploring* matters of scientific concern. Incorporate the proposition/support outlines (pp. 101–104) to help students gather facts, statistics, examples, expert authority, and logic and reasoning for their discussion.

How to use it:

1. After students have read about a controversial issue, introduce them to the discussion web.
2. Select a question based on the reading that can be answered by *yes* and *no*. Write the question in the middle of the form.
3. Allow time for small groups of students (first individually, then as a group) to write down as many *yes* and *no* reasons as they can think of related to the question. Students should write these on the right and left sides, respectively, of the form.
4. Once students have looked at both sides of the issue, they need to agree on a conclusion and then write it in the conclusion box.
5. Ask a spokesperson from each group to share the group conclusion with the rest of the class. Then open the discussion to the rest of the class.

For further discussion of this strategy, see the *TRCA Teacher's Manual*, pp. 160–162.

Notes

Reflection Strategies

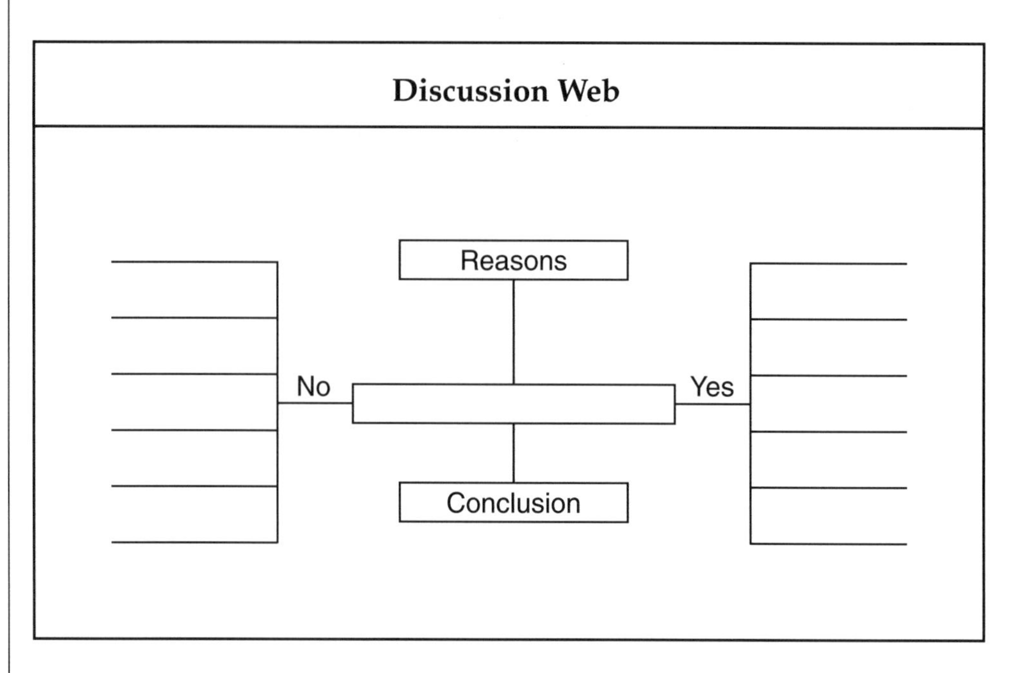

Note. From "The Discussion Web: A Graphic Aid for Learning Across the Curriculum," by D. E. Alvermann, 1991, *The Reading Teacher, 45*(2), pp. 92–99. Reprinted with permission of Donna E. Alvermann and the International Reading Association.

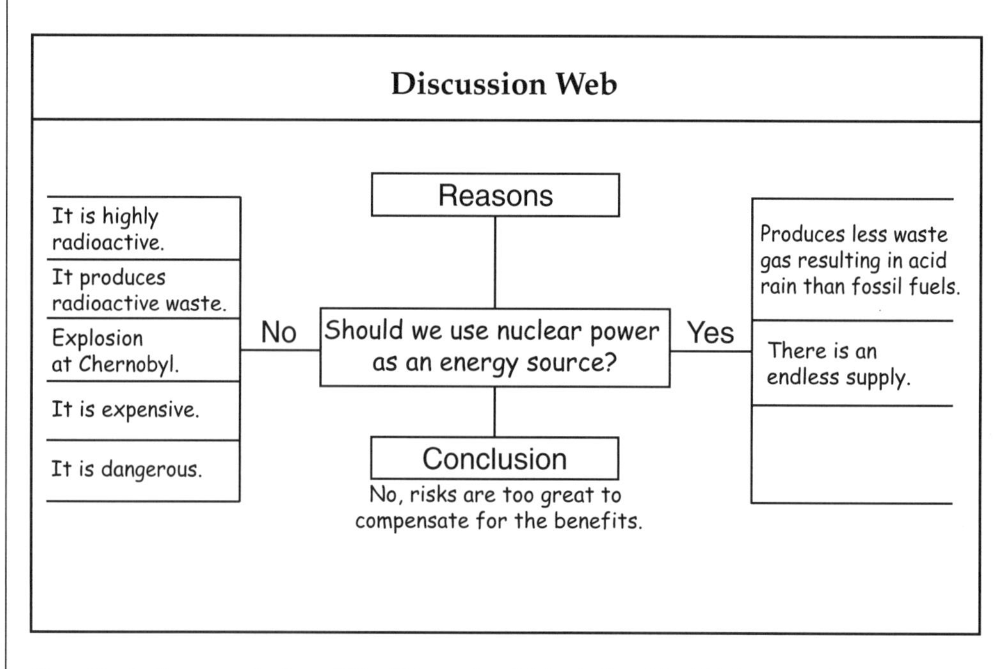

Note. Basic format only from "The Discussion Web: A Graphic Aid for Learning Across the Curriculum," by D. E. Alvermann, 1991, *The Reading Teacher, 45*(2), pp. 92–99. Copyright 1991 by the International Reading Association.

Notes

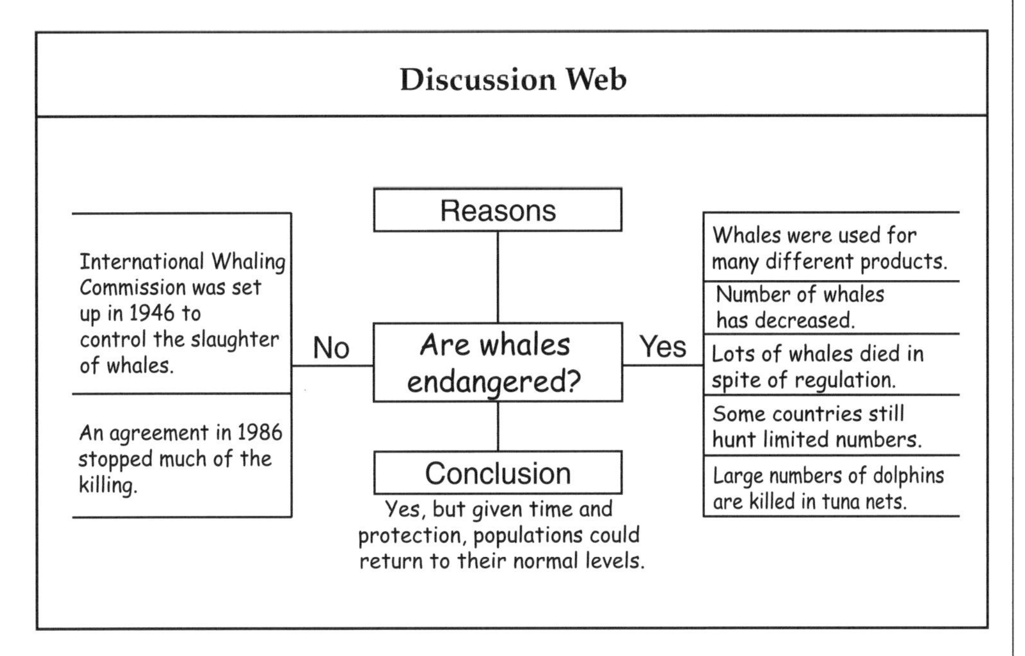

Note. Basic format only from "The Discussion Web: A Graphic Aid for Learning Across the Curriculum," by D. E. Alvermann, 1991, *The Reading Teacher, 45*(2), pp. 92–99. Copyright 1991 by the International Reading Association.

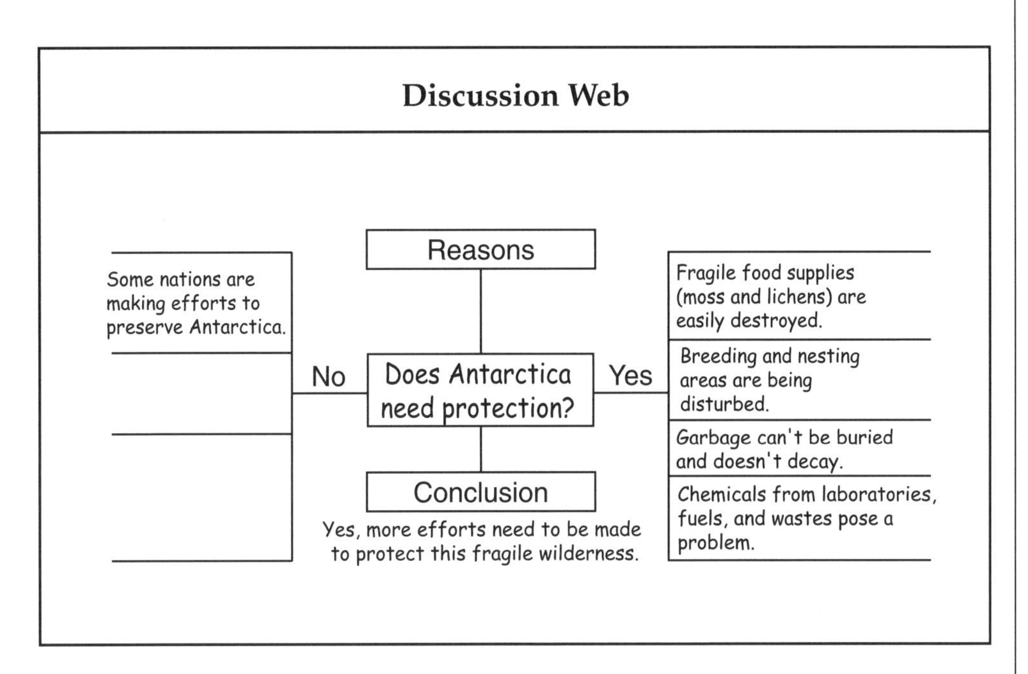

Note. Basic format only from "The Discussion Web: A Graphic Aid for Learning Across the Curriculum," by D. E. Alvermann, 1991, *The Reading Teacher, 45*(2), pp. 92–99. Copyright 1991 by the International Reading Association.

Notes

Reflection Strategies

Preactive
Interactive
Reflective

S-21. Learning Log

What is it?

One of the most effective means of writing-to-learn is keeping a learning log. Learning logs can foster reflection on reading processes and hands-on activities to increase student understanding. Learning logs differ from journals in that they focus on content covered in class, rather than on personal and private feelings. Students may reflect on how they feel, but it is always in relation to what is being studied in class. Santa and Havens (1991) suggest that teachers introduce learning logs to students as a way of writing down their thinking.

How could it be used in science instruction?

Learning log entries can, and should, be incorporated across science lessons. Writing activities can *engage* students' thinking about a concept. Writing can be incorporated to help students *explore* a concept as they collect data. Formulating *explanations* through writing can help students know if they really understand a concept. Students can use writing to *elaborate* on a concept. Writing can be used as a way to self-*evaluate* as students reflect on what they have learned.

How to use it:

1. Assign the topic. A learning log entry can be assigned at any time during class, depending upon the topic and your purpose.
2. Allow students "think time" to consider their response.
3. Give students time to write about the topic.
4. Encourage students to reread their learning log entries at a later date and reflect on how their ideas have changed.

For further discussion of this strategy, please see the *TRCA Teacher's Manual*, pp. 148–150. For further discussion of writing-to-learn, see pp. 154–157 in the *TRCA Teacher's Manual.*

Notes

Learning Log Assignment Examples

Engage

- Why do you think flowers are important?
- Think of an animal. Draw and/or describe its habitat and the specific resources (food, water, shelter, and space) that your animal might need.
- List as many primary consumers as you can.
- If you place an unpeeled orange in a container of water, do you think it will sink or float? On what do you base your prediction?

Explore

- Draw a diagram of your plant and describe how it looks today.
- Draw a diagram of your plant and label these parts: roots, stem, leaves, and flower.
- What attributes or characteristics did you use to classify your objects?
- As you read about the solar system, use the PLAN strategy to organize your understandings.

Explain

- Explain how the experiment you did yesterday relates to what you just read.
- Explain in your own words how energy is transferred from the sun to a green plant.
- Explain in your own words why the bulb lights up in this arrangement of batteries, bulbs, and wires.
- Diagram and explain the relative positions of the sun, moon, and Earth in order to see a full moon from Earth.

Notes

Reflection Strategies

Elaborate

- Create a food chain consisting of the sun, a producer, a primary consumer, a secondary consumer, and either a scavenger or a decomposer.
- Describe other examples of the water cycle that you have seen.
- Where else have you seen examples of the topic you just read about?
- Develop a graphic organizer that illustrates your understanding of germination based on what you have done and what you have read.

Evaluate

- Write about what you have learned during this unit. These terms may help you organize your thoughts: *force, push, pull, gravity, magnetism, motion, friction, work,* and *energy.*
- Recall what you have learned during this unit. These terms may help you organize your thoughts: *sun, moon, Earth, new, full, gibbous, waning, waxing, solar eclipse,* and *lunar eclipse.*
- Summarize what you have learned from your reading about simple machines.
- Summarize what you have learned about incomplete metamorphosis and complete metamorphosis.

Notes

S-22. Question-Answer Relationship (QAR)

What is it?

QAR (Raphael, 1982, 1986) is a strategy that is "designed to demystify the questioning process, providing teachers and students with a common vocabulary to discuss different types of questions and sources of information for answering these questions" (Anthony & Raphael, 1996, p. 319). Four levels of questions are studied during strategy use and practice. Two are text-based QARs:

- "Right There" questions ask students to respond at the literal level; the words used to formulate and answer the question can be found "right there" in the same sentence of the text.
- "Think and Search" questions require students to "think" about how the information or ideas in the text relate to one another, and to "search" through the entire passage they read to find information that applies.

The other QARs could be called knowledge-based because students must use their prior knowledge to answer the question:

- "Author and You" questions require students to combine their prior knowledge with information gleaned from the text to answer the question.
- "On My Own" questions can be answered with information from the students' background knowledge and do not require reading the text.

How could it be used in science instruction?

This strategy focuses on the relationship between questions and answers. It teaches students that addressing different kinds of questions requires different thought processes. Some questions require students to *explore* text to find an answer, some questions require students to *explain* something that they have read, some questions require students to *elaborate* on what they have learned, and some questions ask students to *evaluate* their own thoughts and feelings about an issue.

How to use it:

1. Introduce the strategy by instructing students on each question-answer relationship.
2. Assign short passages to be read from the textbook. As students finish reading each passage, ask them one question from each QAR category. Point out the differences between each question and the kind of answer it requires.
3. After students demonstrate that they understand the differences among the four QAR levels, provide time for students to practice identifying question-answer relationships.
4. Eventually, when reading is assigned in class, students should generate various QARs on their own that they present to the rest of the class for identification and answers.

For further discussion of this strategy, please see the *TRCA Teacher's Manual*, pp. 145–147. For a discussion of a related strategy, concept question chain, see pp. 142–144.

QAR Examples

Right There Questions

- What is a warm-blooded animal?
- Name the device that changes solar energy into electrical energy.
- What is the movement of air from land to water called?
- List the three types of muscles.

Reflection Strategies

Think and Search

- Describe the characteristics of a reptile.
- Compare and contrast *solution* and *suspension*.
- Explain the four kinds of air masses.
- Summarize how the blood moves through the body.

Author and You

- Based on the author's description of mollusks, identify animals that you have seen that fit that classification.
- What evidence have you seen over the past three years that confirms or refutes the information that you just read about global warming?
- Based on the author's information about energy sources, which resource would be most efficient for you to use if you were designing a home?
- Relate what you have read about potential and kinetic energy to experiences that you have had at an amusement park.

On My Own

- Describe a bone or muscle injury that you have experienced.
- What can you do to help stop water pollution?
- Identify constellations that you have observed.
- What are your thoughts about nuclear energy?

Notes

Notes

Reflection Strategies

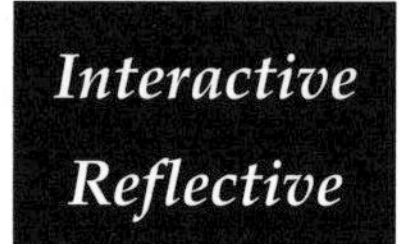

S-23. Questioning the Author (QtA)

What is it?

QtA (Beck, McKeown, Hamilton, & Kucan, 1998) is designed to assist students in their efforts to understand text as they read. The teacher selects a passage based on important concepts students will need to know and constructs *queries*, rather than traditional questions, to build understanding of concepts rather than recall facts. Queries might include:

- What argument or point is the author trying to make?
- What generalizations or conclusions is the author trying to make?
- What is the author describing or explaining?

Query-driven discussions create a community of learners grappling with an author's text and working together to understand it.

How could it be used in science instruction?

Students are more likely to *engage* in reading difficult text if they know that they are part of a community of learners whose goal is to understand the text. This strategy provides students with an opportunity to *explore* their understanding of a topic as they read. It encourages them to *explain* their understanding of a topic to others. It allows them to *elaborate* and to make connections through discussions. It also allows them to self-*evaluate* what they may know and not know about a topic as well as to monitor and adjust their understanding based on the discussion.

How to use it:

1. Analyze and identify important concepts of a text and decide how much of the text should be read at once. Decisions should be based on content, ideas, and information rather than on length of text.

Reflection Strategies

Notes

2. Develop queries or probes that will prompt discussion and build understanding.
3. Instruct students to read the selected passage.
4. Facilitate a query-driven discussion around the passage to grapple with ideas and to build understanding.
5. Provide time for students to understand this process by modeling how you might grapple with ideas to build understanding around a passage.

Examples of Queries

- What comparisons does the author make about the three different insect mouths?
- What is the author's conclusion about the duck-billed platypus?
- How does the author describe *physical properties of matter*?
- Summarize the author's explanation of *photosynthesis*.
- Explain how the circle graph makes sense based on the author's explanation about the number of different kinds of animals in the major animal groups.
- What generalizations is the author trying to make about mixtures?
- What arguments does the author make about using electricity safely?
- How does the experiment that we did relate to the author's descriptions and inferences about water erosion?
- Restate what the author meant by *renewable resource.*
- What is the author's evidence regarding poison in the food chain?
- How do sea breezes and land breezes relate to what the author said about air pressure?
- What is the author's conclusion about smoking?

Notes

Reflection Strategies

S-24. Role/Audience/Format/Topic (RAFT)

What is it?

The RAFT strategy (Santa, 1988) employs writing-to-learn activities to enhance understanding of informational text. Instead of writing a traditional essay explaining a concept learned, students demonstrate their understanding in a nontraditional format. This technique encourages creative thinking and motivates students to reflect in unusual ways about concepts they have read. RAFT is an acronym that stands for

- *Role of the writer.* What is the writer's role: reporter, observer, eyewitness?
- *Audience.* Who will be reading this writing: the teacher, other students, a parent, people in the community, an editor?
- *Format.* What is the best way to present this writing: in a letter, an article, a report, a poem?
- *Topic.* Who or what is the subject of this writing: a famous scientist, a prehistoric cave dweller, a reaction to a specific event?

The RAFT strategy forces students to process information, rather than merely write out answers to questions. Students are more motivated to undertake the writing assignment because it addresses various learning styles.

How could it be used in science instruction?

This writing-to-learn strategy *engages* students in *explaining* what they know about a topic and *elaborating* on the topic in a fun way.

How to use it:

1. Think about concepts or processes that you want students to learn from reading a selected passage. Consider how writing in a fun way may enhance students' understanding of the topic. Include fun topics to write about in learning logs.

Notes

2. Brainstorm possible roles students could assume in their writing.
3. Decide who the audience would be as well as the format for writing.
4. After students have finished reading, identify the role, audience, format, and topic (RAFT) for the writing. Assign the same role for all students, or let them choose from several different roles.

For further discussion of this strategy, see the *TRCA Teacher's Manual*, pp. 151–153.

RAFT Examples

Role	Audience	Format	Topic
Water drop	Other water drops	Travel guide	Journey through water cycle
Bean	Self	Diary	Process of germination
Frog	Tadpole	Letter	Life cycle
Electron	Fourth grade students	Letter	Journey through a parallel circuit
Limestone rock	Cave visitors	Postcard	Chemical weathering process
Statue	Dear Abby readers	Advice column	Effects of acid rain
Trout	Farmers	Letter	Effects of fertilizer runoff
Duck	U.S. Senator	Letter	Effects of oil spill
Star	Self	Diary	Life cycle
Peregrine falcon	Public	News column	Effects of DDT
Red blood cell	Lungs	Thank-you note	Journey through circulatory system
Liver	Alcohol	Complaint	Effects of drinking
Lungs	Brain	Thank-you note	Quitting smoking
Rusty old car	Previous owner	Letter	Chemical change

Note. Basic format only from *Classroom Strategies for Interactive Learning, Second Edition* by D. Buehl, 2001, Newark, DE: International Reading Association.

Notes

Reflection Strategies

S-25. Scored Discussion

What is it?

Scored discussion gives students the opportunity to practice and to evaluate effective discussion skills. A small group of students carry on a content-related discussion after they have read a selection. The teacher and the rest of the class observe and score individual contributions based on predetermined criteria. Students are awarded points for contributing relevant information, using evidence, asking clarifying questions, creating analogies, and encouraging other group members to participate. Negative points are assigned for interruptions, irrelevant comments, and personal attacks. Following the discussion, the teacher and observers provide feedback to discussion members.

How could it be used in science instruction?

This strategy provides students with a structure to *engage* intelligently in public discourse and debate, *exploring* matters of scientific concern.

How to use it:

1. Determine the criteria for a successful discussion and record it for reference during the discussion.
2. Ask students to read a selection around which they can have a discussion.
3. Allow enough time for all students to record their arguments and rationale.
4. Select 6–8 students for the small-group discussion. Explain that the rest of the students will observe and score.
5. Provide time for discussion and scoring.
6. Provide feedback to the discussion members.

For further discussion of this strategy, please see the *TRCA Teacher's Manual*, pp. 163 & 164.

Discussion Score Sheet

Student ______________________________

Class ______________________________

Positive/Productive Behavior	Points
(1) 1. Offers his/her position on a topic	_____ x(1) = _____
(1) 2. Makes a relevant comment	_____ x(1) = _____
(3) 3. Uses evidence to support position	_____ x(3) = _____
(2) 4. Points out contradictions in another person's statements	_____ x(2) = _____
(2) 5. Recognizes when another person makes an irrelevant comment	_____ x(2) = _____
(3) 6. Develops an analogy	_____ x(3) = _____
(1) 7. Asks a clarifying question	_____ x(1) = _____
(3) 8. Uses active listening skills (e.g., rephrases or restates what another student says before commenting)	_____ x(3) = _____

Non-Productive Behavior	Points
(-2) 1. Not paying attention or distracting others	_____ x(-2) = _____
(-2) 2. Interruption	_____ x(-2) = _____
(-1) 3. Irrelevant comment	_____ x(-1) = _____
(-3) 4. Monopolizing	_____ x(-3) = _____
(-3) 5. Personal attack	_____ x(-3) = _____

Total Points:

Positive/Productive Behavior: __________

Non-Productive Behavior: __________

Overall Total: __________

Grade: __________

Note. Adapted from Fred Newmann, School of Education, Curriculum and Instruction, University of Wisconsin.

Bibliography

Anthony, R. J., Johnson, T. D., & Yore, L. D. (1996). Write-to-learn science strategies. *Catalyst, 39*(4), 1016.

Anthony, H. M., & Raphael, T. E. (1996). Using questioning strategies to promote students' active comprehension of content area material. In D. Lapp, J. Flood, & N. Farnan (Eds.), *Content area reading and learning: Instructional strategies* (pp. 307–322). Needham Heights, MA: Allyn & Bacon.

Armbruster, B. B. (1993, January/1992, December). Science and reading. *The Reading Teacher, 46*(4), 346–347.

Armbruster, B. B. (1996). Considerate texts. In D. Lapp, J. Flood, & N. Farnan (Eds.), *Content area reading and learning: Instructional strategies* (pp. 47–57). Needham Heights, MA: Allyn & Bacon.

Baldwin, R. S., Ford, J. C., & Readence, J. E. (1981). Teaching word connotations: An alternative strategy. *Reading World, 21*, 103–108.

Beck, I. L., McKeown, M. G., Hamilton, R. L., & Kucan, L. (1998, Spring/Summer). Getting at the meaning: How to help students unpack difficult text. *American Educator, 85*, 66–71.

Britton, B. K., Gulgoz, S., & Glynn, S. (1992). Impact of good and poor writing. In B. K. Britton, A. Woodward, & M. Binkley (Eds.), *Learning from textbooks: Theory and practice* (pp. 1–46). Hillsdale, NJ: Erlbaum.

Brown, A. L., Day, J. D., & Jones, R. (1983). The development of plans for summarizing texts. *Child Development, 54*, 968–979.

Buehl, D. (1995). Classroom strategies for interactive learning. *Monograph of the Wisconsin State Reading Association*. Scholfield, WI: Wisconsin State Reading Association.

Caverly, D. C., Mandeville, T. F., & Nicholson, S. A. (1995, November). PLAN: A study-reading strategy for informational text. *Journal of Adolescent & Adult Literacy, 39*(3), 190–199.

Costa, A. L., & Garmston, R. J. (1994). *Cognitive coaching: A foundation for renaissance schools*. Norwood, MA: Christopher-Gordon.

Craig, M., & Yore, L. (1996). Middle school students' awareness of strategies for resolving comprehension difficulties in science reading. *Journal of Research and Development in Education, 29*, 226–238.

Davey, B. (1983). Think aloud: Modeling the cognitive processes of reading comprehension. *Journal of Reading, 27*(1), 44–47.

Bibliography

Dickson, S. V., Simmons, D. C., & Kameenui, E. J. (1995). *Text organization: Curricular and instructional implications for diverse learners* (Technical Report No. 19). Eugene, OR: University of Oregon, National Center to Improve the Tools of Educators.

Donahue, D. M. (2000, May). Experimenting with texts: New science teachers' experience and practice as readers and teachers of reading. *Journal of Adolescent & Adult Literacy 43*(8), 728 –739.

Duffelmeyer, F. A., & Baum, D. D. (1992, May). The extended anticipation guide revisited. *Journal of Reading, 35*(8), 654–656.

Finley, F. N. (1991). Why students have trouble learning from science texts. In C. M. Santa & D. E. Alvermann (Eds.), *Science learning: Processes and applications* (pp. 22–27). Newark, DE: International Reading Association.

Frayer, D. A., Frederick, W. C., & Klausmeier, H. J. (1969). *A schema for testing the level of concept mastery* (Technical Report No. 16). Madison, WI: University of Wisconsin, Research and Development Center for Cognitive Learning.

Gillett, J. W., & Temple, C. (1983). *Understanding reading problems: Assessment and instruction*. Boston: Little, Brown.

Herber, H. (1978). *Teaching reading in content areas* (2nd ed.). Englewood Cliffs, NJ: Prentice Hall.

Holliday, W. G. (1991). Helping students learn effectively from science text. In C. M. Santa & D. E. Alvermann (Eds.), *Science learning: Processes and applications* (pp. 38–47). Newark, DE: International Reading Association.

Holloway, J. H. (1999, October). Improving the reading skills of adolescents. *Educational Leadership*, 80–81.

Jenkins, J. R., Stein, M. L., & Wysocki, K. (1984). Learning vocabulary through reading. *American Education Research Journal, 21*(4), 767–787.

Johnson, D. D., & Pearson, P. D. (1984). *Teaching reading vocabulary* (2nd ed.). New York: Holt, Rinehart and Winston.

Jones, B. F., Palincsar, A. S., Ogle, D. S., & Carr, E. G. (1987). *Strategic teaching and learning: Cognitive instruction in the content areas*. Alexandria, VA, and Elmhurst, IL: Association for Supervision and Curriculum Development and North Central Regional Educational Laboratory.

Madrazo, G. M., Jr. (1997, March). Using trade books to teach and learn science. *Science and Children, 34*(6), 20–21.

Bibliography

Marzano, R. J., Pickering, D. J., & Pollock, J. E. (2001). *Classroom instruction that works: Research-based strategies for increasing student achievement.* Alexandria, VA: Association for Supervision and Curriculum Development.

McTighe, J., & Lyman, F. T. (1988). Cueing thinking in the classroom: The promise of theory-embedded tools. *Educational Leadership, 45*(7), 18–24.

Misulis, K. (1997). Textbook comprehension strategies. *Science Scope, 21*(4), 39–43.

Moss, B., Leone, S., & DiPillo, M. L. (1997, October). Exploring the literature of fact: Linking reading and writing through information trade books. *Language Arts, 74*(6), 418–429.

National Research Council. (1996). *National science education standards.* Washington, DC: National Academy Press.

National Research Council. (2000). *Inquiry and the national science education standards: A guide for teaching and learning*. Washington, DC: National Academy Press.

Nelson, G. D. (1999, October). Science literacy for all in the 21st century. *Educational Leadership, 57*(2), 14–17.

Ogle, D. (1986, February). The K-W-L: A teaching model that develops active reading of expository text. *The Reading Teacher, 39,* 564–570.

Ogle, D. (1989). The know, want to know, learning strategy. In K. D. Muth (Ed.), *Children's comprehension of text* (pp. 205–223). Newark, DE: International Reading Association.

Palincsar, A. S., & Brown, A. L. (1985). Reciprocal teaching: Activities to promote "reading with your mind." In T. L. Harris & E. J. Cooper (Eds.), *Reading, thinking, and concept development* (pp. 147–158). New York: College Board Publications.

Powell, G. (1980, December). *A meta-analysis of the effects of "imposed" and "induced" imagery upon word recall.* Paper presented at the annual meeting of the National Reading Conference, San Diego, CA.

Raphael, T. E. (1982). Question-answering strategies for children. *The Reading Teacher, 36,* 186–190.

Raphael, T. E. (1986). Teaching question-answer relationships, revisited. *The Reading Teacher, 39,* 516–522.

Robinson, F. (1961). *Effective study*. New York: Harper & Row.

Bibliography

Roth, K. J. (1991). Reading science texts for conceptual change. In C. M. Santa & D. E. Alvermann (Eds.), *Science learning: Processes and applications* (pp. 48–63). Newark, DE: International Reading Association.

Rutherford, F. J., & Ahlgren, A. (1990). *Science for all Americans.* New York: Oxford University Press.

Santa, C. M. (1988). *Content reading including study systems.* Dubuque, IA: Kendall-Hunt.

Santa, C. M., & Havens, L. T. (1991). Learning through writing. In C. M. Santa & D. E. Alvermann (Eds.), *Science learning: Processes and applications* (pp. 122–133). Newark, DE: International Reading Association.

Santa, C. M., Havens, L. T., & Harrison, S. (1996). Teaching secondary science through reading, writing, studying, and problem solving. In D. Lapp, J. Flood, & N. Farnan (Eds.), *Content area reading and learning: Instructional strategies* (pp. 165–180). Needham Heights, MA: Allyn & Bacon.

Schoenbach, R., Greenleaf, C., Cziko, C., & Hurwitz, L. (1999). *Reading for understanding: A guide to improving reading in middle and high school classrooms.* San Francisco: Jossey-Bass.

Schwartz, R. (1988, November). Learning to learn vocabulary in content area textbooks. *Journal of Reading, 32,* 108–117.

Stahl, S. A., & Fairbanks, M. M. (1986, Spring). The effects of vocabulary instruction: A model-based meta-analysis. *Review of Education Research, 56*(1), 72–110.Stauffer, R. G. (1969). *Developing reading maturity as a cognitive process.* New York: Harper & Row.

Stauffer, R. G. (1969). *Developing reading maturity as a cognitive process.* New York: Haper & Row.

Tchudi, S. N., & Huerta, M. C. (1983). *Teaching writing in the content areas: Middle school/ junior high.* Washington, DC: National Education Association.

Tolman, M. N., Hardy, G. R., & Sudweeks, R. R. (1998, May). Current science textbook use in the United States. *Science and Children, 35*(8), 22–25.

Vacca, R. T., & Vacca, J. L. (1993). *Content area reading (4th ed.).* New York: HarperCollins.

Vacca, R. T., & Vacca, J. L. (1999). *Content area reading: Literacy and learning across the curriculum (6th ed.).* Menlo Park, CA: Longman.

Yore, L. D., Shymansky, J. A., Henriques, L., Chidsey, J. L., & Lewis, J. O. (1997). *Reading-to-learn and writing-to-learn science activities for the elementary classroom.* Retrieved June 1, 2001 from http://www.ed.psu.edu/ci/Journals/97pap1.htm

About the Authors

Mary Lee Barton, M.S. Ed., has worked in the areas of literacy, learning, and professional development for more than 25 years. She brings a wealth of practical classroom experience to her writing and professional development workshops. As a consultant at McREL, Barton coauthored *Teaching Reading in the Content Areas: If Not Me, Then Who?* (2nd ed.) and its supplement, *Teaching Reading in Mathematics.* Her articles "Addressing the Literacy Crisis: Teaching Reading in the Content Areas" and "Motivating Students to Read Their Textbooks" have appeared in the NASSP *Bulletin.* She has trained thousands of teachers and administrators across the country in content-area reading and writing instruction. Currently, Barton is a writer and a business and education consultant in private practice. She trains and provides technical assistance nationally to educators and business clients on literacy issues in education and in the workplace.

As a senior consultant for McREL, Deborah L. Jordan, M.A., has provided technical assistance and training to teachers, curriculum developers, and school administrators nationally over the past four years. Jordan focuses on improving science education through extensive work with standards and their relationship to curriculum, instruction, and assessment. Prior to joining McREL, her 16 years of experience included teaching Chapter I Reading at the middle school level, teaching in the regular elementary classroom, and serving as a district science coordinator.

Workshops Available

McREL delivers training and consultation on *Teaching Reading in the Content Areas: If Not Me, Then Who?* to teachers, reading specialists, staff developers, and administrators.

The **Teachers Workshop** (designed for upper elementary, middle, and high school educators) provides an overview of content area reading instruction; engages participants in applying vocabulary, reading, and discussion strategies to specific content covered in their classrooms; and offers practical suggestions on integrating these strategies into existing curricula.

The **Training-of-Trainers Workshop** is designed for teachers who have a background in reading or who have completed the Teachers Workshop. Participants delve more deeply into critical conceptual ideas underlying the teaching of content area reading skills; receive guidelines for facilitating adult learning; discuss training issues, questions, and concerns; share and critique training plans for teaching content area reading strategies; and discuss schoolwide implementation planning.

The **Teaching Reading in Mathematics Workshop** is designed specifically for mathematics teachers. Participants will examine vocabulary, informational text, and reflection strategies that can help them effectively teach mathematics.

The **Teaching Reading in Science Workshop** is designed specifically for science teachers. Participants will examine vocabulary, informational text, and reflection strategies that can help them effectively teach science.

For more information about scheduling workshops and consulting services, contact McREL at 303.337.0990.